MW00623552

My Life as a Cactus

Tales of a Rookie Reporter in
Mexico

Diane Asitimbay

CULTURELINK PRESS | SAN DIEGO

My Life as a Cactus,
Tales of a Rookie Reporter

ISBN: 978-0-9759-2761-8

Library of Congress Control Number: 2023906876

Published in the United States by Culturelink Press, San Diego, CA
Printed in the United States of America

www.dianeasitimbay.com

To Mexico, with love.

CONTENTS

CONTENTS

"Como México, no hay dos."

"There's only one Mexico."

1

The Perfect Plan

A thunderstorm shook apartment 6B. New York style, of course. Flashes of lightning. Rumbles of thunder. Howls of wind. When the hurricane of rain dropped from the sky, it fell so hard on apartment 6B that it knocked me off the sofa. "Thuddy crap," I said, while visions of toy-sized Marcelos danced in my head.

It was clearly a sign. I needed to wish Marcelo Merry Christmas in person.

I turned the TV off. The program I had been watching was the boringest ever. A fake Yule log flickered flames all night to the sound of Christmas carols.

At 5 a.m., a normal woman from Queens would make her way to her bed and crawl under the covers in this kind of weather. My brain, however, was missing a bit of gray matter so I put on my tight black dress, a new pair of boots, a sexy bra, and set out to surprise the love of my life at his workplace in New Jersey. I glanced at my watch. Five-thirty.

Next, I climbed into the back seat of a cab.

"I need to be there by seven," I told the cabbie, slamming

the door on the gusts of wind that whipped the streets. "When my boyfriend gets off work."

He peered at me from the rear-view mirror. "Long ways to go to New Jersey. In dis weather."

My feet swished in my shoes. "I know." Trickles of mascara ran off my cheek. "But I'm all set."

The cabbie crawled along the road. The cabbie turned the radio down when the announcer warned of flash floods. "Weatherman never right. This time, he right. Very right," he said, wagging his finger in the air with authority.

We bobbed down the highway, splashing water in all directions, the windshield wipers thrashing in a *schwump schwump schwump*. "Look at the bright side." I leaned forward, "you get a free car wash."

Silence. Hunched over the steering wheel, the eyes of the cabbie were glued to the road.

I ventured into a possible one-way conversation. "You know the guy I'm going to see? We've been together for seven years."

"Eh?"

"Do you believe he has to work on Christmas? I haven't seen him in two weeks."

"He no wait for better weather?"

"Oh, he has no idea I'm coming. It's a surprise."

"Surprise? I no like surprise. Maybe he no like surprise."

"Well, my mind's made up." I had no idea what other twenty-eight-year-olds do when their long-time boyfriends moved to another city, but I was surprising mine at his work. No matter how hard the wind was shrieking out there. No matter how wide the Hudson River. Okay, so the Hudson River is only a mile wide. I'd swim across it, neck-high in municipal and industrial waste for Marcelo.

We crossed the George Washington Bridge into New Jersey. The closer we got to Newark, the harder my heart pumped. I reviewed *The Plan*. I would show up at the hospital where Marcelo was working and surprise him as soon as he got off his graveyard shift. Arriving in torrential rains, all the way from Queens with drippy hair and loaded down with his favorite *tamales*, he'll say to himself, what better proof of love? Why, he had just told me last week that the two of us had a future together, but he didn't want to rush it. Who knows? He might even be inspired to pop the "M" word so I would be getting married before collecting my social security. After all, it was the season for miracles.

"You make taxi stink," the cabbie said without glancing over his shoulder. "What you got there?"

"Homemade hot sauce," I said, tightly holding the plastic bowl of hot sauce on my lap so it wouldn't spill. It was filled to the brim and a little bit of sauce was already leaking. "It must be the onions and cilantro." I had bought Marcelo's favorite *tamales* at Adelita's Mexican restaurant in Jackson Heights.

The driver made a quick turn and the tub of sauce slid and leaked even more and dribbled down my coat. "Phew, now I smell like onions and garlic.

"Too early for stink in taxi."

"I can't wait to see the look in his eyes when I show up."

"What if he not there?"

"Not there?" I shifted in my seat, wiping off my coat. "Oh, he'll be there." Why wouldn't he be? He's earning holiday pay.

Marcelo had just called me at midnight. His phone call was solid proof he missed me too. He cooed, "Merry Christmas, baby, I wish you were here, right next to me, so I could hold and kiss you. It's been too long since I've seen you."

Too long? It had been two weeks since the last time we saw each other. The important thing was that Marcelo *thought* two weeks was too long. Now his wish would come true. We'd be together again, all day just like old times. Like the seven years we had lived together before we had our big fight and he moved to New Jersey. We had lived in each other's seams and pockets we were so close. I closed my eyes and could taste his lips. His kisses. Slurpy, sloppy and so sensational that I called him "Hot Lips." He loved my deep, suck-his-tongue-kisses, too, and that's why he called me "Frenchy."

"I should charge you extra for a new one," the cabbie said,

jabbing at his air freshener which dangled from his rear-view mirror in the form of a Christmas tree.

The windows were rolled up tight and it was raining too hard to roll them down. The odor of onions and garlic had nowhere to go.

"Sorry about that," I said.

"Sorry no make stink go away."

A few minutes later, the cabbie splashed into the parking lot of the hospital, flicked the meter off and shamelessly announced, "two-hundred and fifty dollar."

"Two-hundred and fifty dollars? I should report you to Metropolitan Transit authorities for grand theft."

"They tell you price on phone—"

"They said $220—"

"They know how hard is raining? How long time to get here?" He scrawled on a clipboard while a voice crackled onto his radio. He tapped his palm twice against his chest. "From Somalia."

I handed him a wad of bills, and patted my purse twice. "From Brokeville."

"Brookville? I know where. In Queens, right?"

"Yeah, Queens."

Counting the bundle of twenties, the cabbie's mood suddenly changed. He flashed me a loopy grin, kissed the wad and stuffed it in his pocket. "Today ezz Christmas for family and I'm not even Christian!"

"A very Merry Christmas." I shoved open the squeaky door of the cab with my hip.

Jumping over puddles in the parking lot, I sprinted toward the hospital entrance. It was almost seven o'clock. What if Marcelo had left early?

When the automatic doors flew open, I shook the water off like a puppy and snuck past the lady at the main desk. She was in the middle of talking to a family that I couldn't wait for her to—

"Hey—where you slinking off to?" the voice of the receptionist floated over the desk.

"Um . . . I need to find someone."

"You're wetting my floor. You need to bring your drippy self back here and check in. Where you off to?"

"Alcohol Rehab. Listen, I'm surprising my boyfriend for Christmas. I'm his present, and flipped off my hood. "See?" The loops of my red satin ribbon tied around my head with a giant bow drooped. My ribbon tails sagged.

The receptionist sprang from her chair, waved off the family she had been talking to, and took a full stride ahead of me. "Follow me. I gotta see this."

We hurried down the hospital corridor until we reached the nurses' station where I spotted Marcelo. Standing with his back toward us at the counter, he was talking to someone seated at the station. *In the flesh.* I came so lit up when I spotted him that my eyeball sockets were shooting twinkle-twinkle little stars.

Even from my back view, in two weeks, I had completely forgotten how handsome he was. The wild curly hair, the lean legs, the perfectly formed butt, the best-looking body ever issued to a human being. With that physique, I thought, he should have been an underwear model. I tugged at the receptionist's blouse and tilted my nose toward Marcelo.

She mouthed, "That's him?"

I nodded.

She raised her penciled-in eyebrows even higher. "Wow."

I smothered a giggle. "He's even better from the front."

Now for my grand entrance. *Wait a minute.* I hadn't thought about how to surprise him exactly. I knew I had to be dramatic, so I cleared my throat, but before I could muster a *Ta-da! I'm here!* Marcelo had whirled around. The moment he caught sight of me, I went all goose fleshy. "Me!" was all I managed to squeak. Or maybe "Marry Me!" or was it "Merry Christmas?" Whatever it was, Marcelo's reaction was nowhere near the jaw dropping "I can't-believe-it's-you" or the honey-voiced "Merry Christmas, darling!" that I had been waiting for. He muttered a quick goodbye to his colleagues, grabbed my elbow and led me outside. At the hospital entrance, a pudgy curly-haired blonde rushed up to him, and before I could say a word,

Marcelo announced, "Sara, I'd like you to meet my wife."

"Wife?"

"Yeah, wife."

My jaw dropped and hung, and then swung there like a door on a broken hinge. The wife didn't stick her hand out for a handshake and neither did I.

"Who's she?" the wife asked.

"Sara."

"Sara, who?"

"Sara?" a faraway voice called my name.

Numb. My hand flew to my chest to see if my heart was still beating 'cause it felt like a hole inside there.

"How did you get here?" That faraway voice was Marcelo's.

An automatic word tumbled out. "Taxi."

"I'll drive you to the nearest train station."

"But we're supposed to be at my parents' by noon," the wife whined. "Who is she? Do we have to take her?"

As if by remote control, I marched across the parking lot. One foot after the other. When a garbage can appeared, my tub of hot sauce and plate of tamales crashed to the bottom of it.

I slipped into the back seat of Marcelo's raggedy Toyota. Squished between two stacks of wrapped Christmas gifts. Resting my head on the pillowy packages, I let it all go.

Giant tears rolled down my face. My chest heaved in and out. A few choking sounds. Before I could smother it, a whopping wail rattled the windows.

The whole car ride, the wife ignored me. Not a word. Never said "Excuse me, he's taken." She had to know the woman in the backseat believed she had found her mate, her butter on her bread, her peak on her mountain, and all that jazz.

Once I looked up from my puddle of humiliation, I caught a blurry glimpse of Marcelo through the rear-view mirror. A little smirk flickered across his face.

How could he? My beloved Marcelo?

By the time we reached the train station, I was nothing but a sopping washcloth. The gift wrappings on their Christmas packages were soaked through and through and were peeling off, too. I would go out—not gracefully—it was too late for that under the circumstances, but at least with a bang. Before the car reached a complete stop, I managed to yank open the door, pluck my soppy self from the back seat, and give the door a big wham. Then I was off and running as fast as my legs would go into the station.

2

Escape

B ack at my apartment, I fell onto the couch, face first. My brain churned. I should slurp a fishbowl of wine, but no, better yet, fill up a fishbowl with tears. Oh, I cried and cried and cried and cried some more. I cried so much that I turned into the woman in Picasso's *Weeping Woman with Handkerchief,* except I clutched a New York Yankee towel to wring out my tears.

And then there was the issue of how I came to have the brains of an eggplant. After twenty-eight years of building a complex neural circuitry, I had lost sight of our relationship. My vision had hovered around 13/13 on a scale of 20/20 being perfect vision, legally qualifying me as blind.

Never read *Cosmopolitan* or *People,* but I should have. These girly magazines were waiting for me in the hair salon. They have columns to warn you, like "Ten Signs That He Is Cheating on You." If I had read them, I would have asked the questions that I was supposed to be asking: *Why wasn't I ever invited to his apartment? Why didn't he come to my place in the daytime?* He told me it was because he worked at night and slept days. And I believed him. *Why did every conversation about commitment turn into a dead end?*

Suddenly, I sat up on the couch with a clear thought. I know. I'll escape. That's what I'll do. Run off to some remote island in the South Pacific named Yap or Funafuti, where the sun would bake my skin 365 days of the year. Where I'd bathe in papaya juice at night. Where I'd absolutely, definitively forget Marcelo. Somewhere far, far away. With a glimmer of hope, I returned to my computer and looked up tropical travel packages on the Internet. All I found were pathetic travel packages for lovey-dovey couples, with cruel names like "Heavenly Honeymoons in Hawaii" and "Temptation Resorts in the Caribbean." "Ugh!" Where were the "Recently Dumped Specials" when you needed them? Besides, I had no money to go somewhere far away because of my low salary as a copy editor. First, I had to save up for it. For now, somewhere far away would be around the corner to Flushing Meadow Park.

* * *

After seven months of crying myself to sleep every night and not eating, I now weighed approximately two pounds, not including my mound of curls piled on top of my head. But I was going to Mexico City. I had scraped enough money to go for two weeks. My vacation had only one lofty goal – to be able to fall asleep without tears when I got back to Queens.

Out came my suitcase. In went the clothes, at least the ones that I still fit or I could swim in. In went rolls and rolls and rolls of smashed toilet paper. If Customs officials accuse me of toilet paper smuggling, it will give me a chance to raise the whole shortage-of-toilet paper issue I had read about in Lonely Planet.

In went the all-important pack of Marlboro cigarettes. (same brand Marcelo used to smoke). I took out a big black magic marker, crossed out the warning label: Smoking Is Dangerous to Your Health and in big black letters, printed "ESCAPE FROM DESTRUCTION! MEN ARE FATAL HAZARDS TO YOUR HEALTH." I vowed to carry this pack of cigarettes around in my purse everywhere I went as a reminder to stay away from men.

* * *

In two weeks, a lot can happen. And oh boy, did it. My little vacation turned my whole world upside down. While in Mexico City, on a whim, I applied to an English-language newspaper. They gave me a Spanish translation test, and when I passed, they offered me a job as a staff reporter. So I flew back to New York right away to quit my job and say goodbye to my cousin Alex.

Now back in New York again and packed, this was really the goodbye. Goodbye to New York and the beginning of a new life, a "new job with potential." Goodbye to stinky subways. Goodbye to a soul-sucking job. Goodbye to Marcelo skeletons.

I wouldn't miss anything, really.

Okay, I would miss the Chinese take-out from Jimmie Chang's. Most of all, I would miss my cousin Alex. I'd grown up with cousin and loved him as a brother. My only family in New York. I felt guilty leaving, too. Guarding the secret that he was gay and he had cancer. He wasn't treating his cancer but made me swear a cousinly oath to keep his situation under wraps from the rest of our conservative Catholic family in Michigan. Meanwhile, his health was getting worse. He said chemotherapy only prolonged things and had terrible side effects. That he didn't want to lose his hair and eyebrows. I wanted to be there for him.

When I broke the news that I was moving to Mexico, I didn't go into the details. I just told him that Marcelo and I broke up.

"I don't want to talk about it," I added.

"That bad, huh?"

"Worse."

"He left you then."

"No. Way worse. He got married."

"Naw. Scum.

"Secretly married."

"Want me to find him and beat 'em up? You give me permission to beak his legs?

"Nah. But you see why I can't live in New York anymore? There are Marcelo skeletons everywhere."

"Escaping from problems runs in the family," Alex said.

"I'm not escaping."

"Are too."

"Am not. I'm going to work there. I won't be lying on a sun-soaked beach somewhere in Cancún sipping margaritas."

"If that's what you need to do, that's what you need to do. I'll take care of your apartment. Sublet it. I'll even store your Spanish books in my office. In the coat closet."

"My books?" Oh, yes, I had to keep those. I seriously owned some of the best of the Spanish classics of literature. I found intellectually stimulating authors–especially Spanish-language authors– incredibly sexy. My major crush was on Miguel Hernandez, the lion of Spanish literature even though he was way older than me. And he lived in Mexico!

"Are you listening?" Alex asked.

"Yeah, why?"

"As soon as you get settled in Mexico, I'll come visit you."

I jabbed him in the ribs. "You better come visit me. 'Cause I'll miss you."

"You know, cuz, you got to love yourself first. What I mean is, you don't need a man for your happiness."

"Look at you, Mr. Philosopher, all of a sudden."

"Just saying. I know about what love can do to people. How it can make us forget about ourselves. It happened to me. And I saw it happen to you with him. You were always trying to help Marcelo with his addictions. Remember? Trying to stop his smoking and drinking? You weren't looking out for yourself."

I poked him in the ribs again. "You done with your pearly bits of wisdom?"

He poked me back. "Now go put that male phantom to bed."

* * *

Gone. After saying goodbye to Alex, I vanished, real Houdini-like.

Slipped through the cracks of New York. Seven years of collected crapola in the trash. Not a trace of Sara Tortellini except for some books crammed into a closet at the cousin's house.

When the plane circled to land, I smooshed my nose against the cold window and took it all in:

Mexico City sprawled below like a postcard.

Hello, new home. Tiny, far-away houses and toy cars on the streets peeked through the smog. The city's landmarks came into view in dim nebulous shapes and appeared vaguely familiar from my visit two weeks earlier. I recognized The Latin American Tower, Bellas Artes, and Reforma Boulevard. I think I even spotted the One Yelp Hotel popping out of the haze but I couldn't be sure.

* * *

Once the plane landed, I snagged a taxi, and checked into the cheapo One Yelp Star Hotel. This time, boisterous backpackers had invaded the hotel. I had bigger things to think about, like securing my job after being hired on a handshake two weeks earlier. I wanted the new boss to swear to me on a stack on steaming tamales, but I don't think he would have, so I settled for a laser beam stare instead.

Dumping my luggage in my room as fast as I could, I headed to *The Observer*. I needed to see if my prospective boss would remember this foreign underling he promised to hire.

I hurried past the fashionista receptionist in the newspaper lobby, shot up the elevator, and sank into a chair outside the managing editor Guido's office. A torturous twenty minutes went by. I had just tossed my whole life into a dumpster for a job I hadn't even secured properly yet. Sara, you are dumb. Get ready to go home. By the time Guido finally came out of his glass cage, I had bitten off all my ingrown cuticles and had returned to Queens to join the Dumpster Divas, climbing into stinky metal boxes to retrieve plastic bottles.

He threw his arms up in the air as if shocked to see me again. "So you made it back. What do you know?" He crushed my frozen fingers in his hands. "Have you moved here?"

"Yeah, I have, I mean . . . here I am." I squelched the impulse to blurt out he'd better hire me or else. "And I'm ready to work."

"Good, I've been waiting for you." He was a short-necked man, with bulging but friendly eyes peering out from behind those glasses.

I blew out half a lungful of air. Not all of it, though. Not until I uncapped my pen, not until I filled out a form for wages, and signed on the dotted line did I empty the full carbon dioxide tank. "When do I start?"

Guido waved me through a doorway. "I'll show you production and then you can get started."

Among the noisy machines in the basement, Guido told me about the ins and outs of the fifteen newspaper dailies in Mexico City, *The Observer* was the only English daily with a circulation of 50,000. "Even though it's small," Guido said, "your leaders read our newspaper. A million and a half Americans live in Mexico, you know that? News is sacred here."

"I see." What was this leading to?

Guido's eyes zeroed in on mine. "Your job is to edit copy, translate and report news. Reporters are expected to report favorably on government activities. Those who don't will be asked to leave by the Gobernación."

"Gubernación?" I asked in a hushed tone.

"The Mexican equivalent of the State Department. You newcomers should learn this fast. You don't want to be like that reporter who exposed the Mexican treatment of Guatemalan refugees on the southern border. He was given two days to leave the country."

"You mean leave— as in *deported?*"

Guido nodded.

"Oh." I'd gone through a whole lot of trouble to move to Mexico. Now my boss was hinting at deporting me if I failed to report stories in a politically correct manner.

"Journalists possess something valuable. Information. Information gives them prestige. Prestige inspires awe. You understand?"

"Got it," I said. "Information. Prestige. Awe. Hmm . . .what about salary?"

"You'll be paid in pesos. Starting salary is three thousand, one hundred pesos a week."

The three-thousand part sounded like a lot of money, but I had a gut feeling it might not be. "Um . . . do I have medical insurance?"

Guido chuckled. "Ay, no. But if you get sick, there's an in-house doctor downstairs. He'll give you something for amoebas and birth control."

"Oh, that's convenient."

At the end of the tour, I followed Guido into the newsroom where he noisily cleared his throat. Reporters' conversations instantly stopped as if he were a drill sergeant blowing a whistle. Guido sliced the air in a melodramatic wave. "Sara, here are your fellow reporters."

All eyes darted to me.

"Ahm . . . hello, everyone," I gave a bit of sideways hello and scanned the sea of faces where I met several wide, toothy grins. I felt like fake royalty receiving a 21-gun salute from the press corps.

Guido motioned to a middle-aged man sitting the closest to us. "This is Enrique, the city editor. You'll be reporting directly to him."

Enrique rose to offer his hand in an elaborate and extended handshake. The corners of his lips cured up into his mustache. "*Encantado de conocerla*. Nice to meet you." He oozed a formal Mexican air. Guido addressed the reporters in the newsroom in English, but Enrique replied in flourishing niceties to me in Spanish, so it appeared that I would be speaking Spanish to my city editor. I told myself it would be good practice.

Guido went on. "I want all of you to welcome our new reporter. Meet Sara . . . er . . . sorry, I don't remember your last name."

"Tortellini. Sara is fine." We went round and round, one by one, with reporters telling their first and last names and some other stuff in between. After three elaborate introductions and a string of names that all ran together, I only remembered the last guy piping up in a twang, "I'm Dave from Texas." Of course, he stood out from the others because of the twang and his simple, one-name introduction.

I nodded once more and said, "Good to meet everyone." An awkward lull followed.

"You can go back to writing your stories," Guido said to the reporters, "and your deadlines."

"Thank you, I muttered under my breath. I felt so embarrassed standing there like that, in front of everybody for twenty minutes, while Guido went on and on.

Guido snatched a stack of stapled papers from Enrique's wire basket. "Here's a press conference you should go to tonight."

I gripped the big, fat press release, lightly shook it a couple of times to get an idea of how much it weighed. Two-pounds at least. Ha ha. "Just this?"

"That's it," Guido said.

I flipped through the pages. Seven pages long, 9-point print, and *in Spanish*. A voice inside of me screamed *Help! Get me outta here!*

"Don't worry." Guido gave me a couple of hearty pats on the back. "If you don't get much out of the press conference, just translate this release and you should be set."

"I'll give it my best." It never occurred to me that Guido might be psychic. Or maybe I wore my emotions so plainly that I might as well be a human emoji.

After Guido finally trotted off, I sank into a chair. I dug into my wallet, pulled out a Mexican bill and unfolded it. One-hundred Mexican pesos. Roughly five U.S. dollars. Puny and foreign. I should figure out what I'd be making in dollars. My mind began calculating. Let's see . . . one thousand, three hundred pesos per week . . ."

"Sara?" Someone called my name. My final tally. *One hundred fifty dollars a week.* That was my salary. Worse than my last copy editor's job, which was three-cents over minimum wage. "Oh my God. I'd make more money baby-sitting," I mumbled. I definitely couldn't tell Mom and Dad. Or any of my friends. Why didn't I just take the two-week vacation and leave, then try to forget Marcelo in a more economical way? I buried my head in my arms on the computer keyboard. *Mexico is not for the meek and mild. Mexico is not for the meek and mild.* Somehow, repeating these words to myself made me feel stronger inside.

"Sara?" That same voice. Raspy like sandpaper. This time I recognized it. It belonged to the older woman with short hair the color of a gingersnap. She wore funky oversized glasses with frames matching her red lipstick.

"Sara?" said the voice now at my elbow. That same sixtyish woman. I looked up. She was wrapped in an expensive-looking dress and her neck was covered in a scarf with initials I didn't recognize.

"Yes?"

"I'm Malena Cardenas, remember? I write the society column."

"A society column? Where you write about weddings and fundraisers of famous people?"

"That's right. Believe it or not, my gossip column *'Charla y Chismes,'* has survived the Internet and God knows how many celebrity bloggers. Other columns have disappeared into the *Lifestyle & Culture* section, but not mine."

"So, you must know a lot of people."

"Oh, yes. I'm a name dropper. That's my job. I go to all the parties, especially those of the foreign community."

"Great. You are friendful, and I just arrived, and am friendless. Kind of evens us out, doesn't it?"

Her chuckle was like a cough. "You going to tell me where you're from?"

Wow, she gets right to the point, doesn't she? "New York.

Well, originally from Michigan, but I was living in New York before moving here."

"Well, I was born in Mexico City. Came from a diplomat family. That's how I learned my English. How did you learn Spanish?"

"College."

Malena rasped. "You smoke?"

"Nope. Hate it." I figured if she was going to be blunt about it, it might as well be mutual.

"That's too bad. We could have a cigarette downstairs. You came to the wrong city if you hate smoke."

"Huh?"

"We're famous for our smog."

"For your smog?" I winced. I wanted to say I had already noticed, but I didn't. Well, even if she had the nasty smoking habit, I don't think I will like her. But I could relate to her boldness. New York style. Maybe we could form a bond based on brashness.

"Well, I'd better get back to work," Malena said. "Let me know if you need help." With that, she sauntered back to her computer.

By this time, with all the introductions and commotion of a first day on the job, my head throbbed. Too much newness. I was officially a rookie reporter married to a Mexican newspaper. I had signed on the dotted line of some legal paper, and promised to love and cherish *The Observer* from this day forward, for richer or for poorer, for better or for worse, in sickness and in health.

Oh, what did I just do?? I sat there fingering my press release as if it was my bridal bouquet. What if I didn't like working at the politically correct paper?

Across the room, a bony guy dressed in a white tunic and baggy, pajama trousers, the one with the piercing eyes and hairless chin, was talking to Enrique. On the way back to his desk, he stopped at my computer and thrust out his bony hand. "I'm Ashok, from India. I cover mostly financial news, but some general news."

"Same. I mean, the general news part." He had very little meat on those bones, but his eyes penetrating, dark and as liquidy as squid ink. I wondered if those eyes saw me as possible competition, the new reporter on the block.

"See those girls over there?" With a tilt of his chin, Ashok pointed to two young women standing and chatting at their computers, a couple of stations away. They were looking at each other like they had antennas and were sending radio signals to each other while stealing a glance at me now and then.

"You mean the tight little twosome?"

"Yes."

"The ones who appear to be guarding a deep, dark secret from me?"

"Yeah, those two."

I dreaded hearing any more about the dynamic duo, but asked, "What about them?"

Ashok continued his chin nod in their direction. "The taller one? That's Emma, from London. She covers the music scene and goes to all the music festivals."

"British?" I asked, terror-stricken.

He nodded.

Memories of my high school English teacher Miss Funkelbottom swirled in my brain. She was British. "Absolutely appalling" were her exact words to describe the way I spoke. Said I needed elocution lessons. I studied the critical cream puffs from across the room. "I get a feeling that they don't like me."

"You've only been here an hour. It takes longer for them not to like you. A few days at least."

"I'm not so sure about that. I'm getting these creepy vibes across the newsroom."

"The other one is Kate," he said. "She writes features on the art scene."

"Wait. *Both* are British?" Not only did a British accent reduce me to the babble of a one-year-old, but both of these British women had the crème de la crème assignments, writing art and music features. I know why, too. *I bet the British girls kiss Guido's gluteus maximus.*

"Right. They're best friends."

"Seriously?"

Ashok leaned closer to say in a reverential whisper. "Emma and Kate finish their entire stories in the time it takes the rest of us to write a byline."

"You're kidding me, aren't you? I mean, I might look like a naive *gringa,* right off American Airlines, Flight No. 263 and all—"

"Afraid not."

"How do you know?" I asked.

"I've seen it. With my own eyes."

"*Oh, my God.*" I was doomed. Maybe they were being fed intravenously by the *Oxford* dictionary each night to come up with all those words so fast.

Ashok shook his head. "They make us all look bad."

"Well, it figures," I muttered. *What do you expect? They're British. They put crisp endings on their words. They enunciate their "Ts."*

Ashok then looked at me almost with pity as he turned to leave. "Here, you'll soon learn, it's pretty much everyone on their own. A sink or swim kind of thing."

"Look forward to it," I said. If I wanted to, I could conceal my fear like a diplomat and with my steady voice, I did just that.

I just sat there in a daze for about fifteen minutes or so, letting the idea of a new career soak in. *Now what?* I knew absolutely nothing about news. The only skill I had was putting my hand under my armpit and making that ugly noise, I mean besides reading. Why did I get myself into this mess? Then I remembered why. I was looking for a cure to my near-fatal medical condition commonly known as "heartbreak." And by the looks of things, no cure was imminent. I couldn't throw the thick press release away. Even if it was "official" government news dug up by some slick politician and filtered through a censor committee. *Canned* news. I couldn't throw that garbage away because I *needed* it.

"Is something wrong?" Malena asked, peering over her computer.

"Jet lag, that's all," I mumbled.

"If there is," Malena went on, "you'd better go and tell Guido right away."

I reached for the press release again. "Maybe I should try reading it," I whispered aloud.

"Sara?" Malena asked.

"Yes?"

"Did you say something?"

"Nothing." I feigned a smile. I glanced at the computer screen and back to the press release. I'd translate this thing as fast as I could. Next, I'd figure out how to find a more permanent place, far from the noisy hotel. A quiet place. A place where you get a fine for noise pollution.

* * *

Something smelled fishy. I couldn't quite put my finger on it when I paid a security deposit to my first Mexican landlord and she suddenly said, "I'm recently divorced." Well, it's hard to know what to say when someone says something like that to a total stranger. I wanted to say, "So? I'm heartbroken," but instead, I muttered an "Oh," or something along those lines.

At this point, when I finally got to see inside an apartment and the landlord actually showed up, I was so desperate to get it over with that the landlady could have said she was going to jump off the building and I probably would have replied with an "Oh, that's nice." Since I had no connections to anyone or anything, I had putting up with the noisy one Yelp hotel for three weeks. Even worse, I found out the hotel was a really a love hotel, most of the rooms were rented by the hour for extramarital affairs, a Cheater's Paradise.

So I smiled at the new landlady because I really, really wanted this apartment. The señora added that she'd be keeping her master bedroom in my apartment, so she'd be back to sleep there "sometimes." Her "sometimes" at my place made it all the more mysterious. But I dismissed my misgivings again. I told myself that it was just a weird feeling that comes from sharing an apartment with a total stranger in Mexico.

* * *

A week later, I was deeply into my REM sleep when someone banged on the door to open. "¡*Abre la puerta*!" a male's voice yelled.

I sat up and listened in the pitch dark.

Bang went the door again. "I know you're in there." He slurred his words, sounding drunk.

I leaped out of bed to lock the bedroom door, grabbed the blanket from my bed and pulled it all the way up over my head to muffle the sounds of "I know you're in there."

Several minutes later, the angry outbursts had turned to whimpers, "I still love you. You're still my wife. I need to talk to you." The sound of a slump to the floor and then silence.

I lay there stunned for what seemed like fifty-seven years. At last, the sound of footsteps. When they faded away, I relaxed my grip on the blanket.

Days passed, and no Drunk Husband appeared. Just when I was about to breathe a sigh of relief, after sleeping peacefully several nights, *Thump . . . thump. . . thump* would wake me up followed by a *WHACK* at my door.

Sitting straight up in the darkness, I hardly breathed, hoping the Drunk Husband would think nobody was home (or alive) and go away. Several minutes would pass. Or maybe it was a half hour. He was begging his wife to take him back. It was an eternity each time. After he kicked at the door and bawled about his life of suffering without her, he'd eventually go away.

I lie awake nights asking myself. What are the chances of a Drunk Husband looking for his ex-wife in my apartment? Like one in a zillion. Oh, it was probably only a coincidence, but it didn't feel like that. I sensed Marcelo's ghost. Had he followed me all the way to Mexico? The Drunk Husband sent me chilling reminders. Marcelo's drinking problem was a huge part of the first fight that split us up. After I found mini vodka bottles hiding in the back of cupboards, behind the bedpost, even buried in my bookcase, I had confronted him about it and that's when he went berserk. Just remembering it made me break out in a rash.

I telephoned the señora for help. She never answered the phone and had no voice mail. The next time the Drunk Husband came and launched his act, I wriggled beneath my bed and waited, face down on the floor. When the sobbing was over and the footsteps faded, I crawled out like a turtle poking its head out to take a breath.

Fear and Courage argued with each other those Drunk Husband nights. I thought of hanging a hotel "*Sleeping. Do Not Disturb!*" sign on the doorknob but he might not understand the word "disturb" in English. I even considered going to the butcher and nailing a cow's head to the front door in hopes of scaring off the Drunk Husband the next time he'd come. But I wasn't that brave.

When the Drunk Husband came to bang on the door on another visit, I stiffened in bed, beat down the panic and this time, my curiosity, not courage, trumped fear. I wanted to see what he looked like. Who was this bawling mess?

I slid ever so gently off the bed onto the cold linoleum floor, and scooted an inch or two. The floor creaked. I froze. I nudged an inch or two forward, stopped, and then slid again, holding my breath until I reached the door.

The stairwell was well lit, so as I squinted with one eye pressed to the old-fashioned keyhole, I was half expecting to see a part of a thigh, a leg or an elbow.

A grizzly unshaven face and bloodshot eyes—like a mangy coyote's—stared back. My face went from olive to yellow to white except no one could see it because of the pitch dark. When he let out a couple of snorts and grunts through the closed door, I shimmied across the floor as fast as I could, nose-dived into bed, and yanked the covers over my head.

He must have detected my rustling on the other side of the door. For that night, he stayed longer, begging for his wife to take him back, and then his pleas changed to threats, and he even pounded on the door moaning he was going to die. The rest of the night, I had French kiss nightmares of a camouflaged reptile creature sticking his hideous reptile tongue into my mouth so far that it came out through the back of my skull.

I rolled about in agony for hours before I finally dozed off.

Things went on like this until one day I finally reached the señora on the phone and told her about her ex-husband.

"Oh, he's harmless. He doesn't have the key anymore."

"But don't you think you should talk to him? Tell him there's nobody living here anymore. He's keeping me up all night and I'm tired all day."

"No, I've changed the locks. You're safe, so stop worrying."

Easy for her to say. She was only there "sometimes," which conveniently happened to coincide with the times he didn't appear. Sleepless in Queens over someone else's husband and now sleepless in Mexico City because of someone's ex-husband, I vowed to listen more carefully to the next owner describe the place I might rent. I'd ask a lot more questions. I began combing the newspaper again for a new room to rent. I would never ignore my instincts again.

3

The Three Mexican Commandments

As an outsider, there are certain rules that you are expected to follow unless you want to get into Big Trouble. For example, there are things you know, things you don't know, and things that you don't know but are supposed to know.

Take greetings, for example. I knew nothing about greetings in Mexico before Malena, who I secretly called the "Mexicanologist," because she was teaching me everything I ever wanted to know about Mexican customs even if I wasn't asking. Anyway, Malena informed me on how important greetings were. Greetings are the social grease to make relationships run smooth in Mexico, she explained. Furthermore, she gave me the straight talk on the people you are to greet and proper way to greet them here.

287.

That's the number of times I'd say *buenos días* in a week. I counted them.

First off, you are supposed to start with a ¡*Buenos Días!*

¿Cómo está? A light handshake if you don't know him, a hug if you do. Not only that, as a woman, you're supposed to plant a peck on the cheek or air-kiss those you are greeting by making a little "mwah" sound. Then you're supposed to ask about their families. Next, you're supposed to ask about their general health. Doing all this should be done in the correct order, with the correct dramatic flourish, and in the correct enthusiastic tone. This is very important. When greeting a group of people, it is necessary to greet and shake hands with each person individually, rather than address the group together, no matter how long it takes. You should even greet the store owner with a *¡Buenos Días!* if you walk into a store. If for some reason, you're in a hurry? Well, that's too freaking bad. It's what you are supposed to know and do.

Oh, but wait. There were others things I wasn't supposed to do. For the things I wasn't supposed to do, I didn't get any instructions from Malena or God. I wanted instructions like Moses got. He hiked all the way up to Mount Sinai to get his Tablets and came down carrying a list of shouldn't-dos on hefty slabs.

No divine revelation came to me in a Mexican instructional manual so I learned the hard way the Three Mexican Commandments:

1) Never talk bad about your mother, or anybody else's mother for that matter;
2) Never criticize the Virgin of Guadalupe;
3) Never ever bring up the Mexican-American War.

Believe it or not, "Thou shalt not say mean things about thy mother" was not the Holy Commandment I broke. (Even though my mom permanently annoyed me because she was trying to fix me up with that Michigan boy). No, the Commandment I broke was Commandment Number Three. Never ever bring up the Mexican-American War.

When covering an American Legion event, I wrote a lopsided (actually, an American-sided) version of the Mexican-

American war. Words just flew off my fingertips, rolled out *The Observer* door, and landed on a Mexican festering wound. My article included a quote from an American veteran saying how the U.S. got a whole lot bigger from "winning" the war against the Mexicans. This was back when we suffered from Manifest Destinitus and took half Mexico's territory.

Little did I know that Mexicans were far from the forget-and-forgive mode for a war that happened a hundred and fifty years ago. From the Mexican point of view, we *stole* the territory, not *took* it, *stole* it outright. *Highway robbery. Whole entire states.* Every Mexican can name the stolen goods: California, Nevada, Utah, most of Arizona, about half of New Mexico, about a quarter of Colorado and a small section of Wyoming. To top it off, I learned that Mexicans and Americans call the war different names. Mexicans call the war *the United States' Invasion of Mexico,* or *La Guerra del 47* (The War of 1847). And the U.S. calls it the Mexican-American War, and claims it lasted from 1846 to 1848.

Oh, knew I was in deep, deep muck when Guido called me into his office. He waved a stack of papers in the air like he was swatting flies. "Did you see this?" he shouted and gave me that look.

"What is it?"

He handed me a damning ten-page document listing an alleged thirty-six-point total of errors. "Read it! Just read it!" I leafed through the pages, and my finger paused where someone had circled a paragraph and scrawled "lies" in red ink.

I sank in the chair. "All over the Mexican-American war?"

"It's not a little thing. Don't you see how furious they are?" Guido thundered.

I sucked in air and let it out slowly. "Yeah, well, they are certainly not writing me thank-you notes."

That remark got Guido even more steamed up. He leaped out of his chair and began to pace in a circle around his desk. "I can't believe this! You making jokes! You Americans! Everything a joke! You insulted our readers!"

"I was only reporting on what that American Legion guy

said."

"How come you didn't check the facts?"

"Against what? A history book? Do they give us two sides there?" I handed the document back to him. "Besides, Enrique looked at my article before it came out. He didn't catch any mistakes." A deep pang of guilt went from the bottom of my stomach and shot up to my scalp. *I was blaming Enrique.*

"You know what this means?" Guido slapped the document of corrections.

"Yeah. I should rely on more than one source from now on."

"*That.* Of course, *that.* Besides that?"

"Er . . ."

Guido narrowed his eyes down to slits. "We're going to have to publish these letters, that's what it means. He shuffled papers around his desk. He tossed a letter in the air.

It floated down like a wobbly feather.

"Hell, which ones? I'll have to figure it out."

"Guido, I just reported what the guy told me. I didn't realize, I mean, I had no idea that there might be . . . another side of the story."

"You didn't realize it?" His eyes bulged out of his head. "Did you say you didn't *realize* it?"

"Yeah, I mean, no. I'm so sorry—"

"What about *this* one?" His puffy face got even puffier as he read some of the letter aloud and at the end, yelled: THIS REPORTER SHOULD BE FIRED! Should I fire you? Everybody thinks so."

Fired? Did he say *fired?*

I said nothing. My head bent, I studied the diamond pattern on the tiled floor, looking real repentant. Silence. More silence. I let the silence sink in so my boss would calm down a bit.

Guido finally sat down. He took off his glasses and rubbed his hand over his eyes. "Hmm . . . Do you realize what you did, Sara?"

"Now I do. Yes. These letters are serious," I said in a strangled sort of voice.

"Very," Guido echoed. "*The Observer* has a print run of 50,000 copies. Making a mistake in print means making 50,000 mistakes."

"I'm sorry. Really, I am." I tried to sound meek and mousy. Even with a sense of humbleness, I sensed that soon I would be driven to the airport and never invited back. Like that deported reporter Guido had told me about on the very first day. The one who reported on Guatemalan refugees.

I scanned the room. No place to hide. I needed a trap door right about then, where I push a button, the trap door opens and *baam! There goes Sara.* I guess expressing another round of remorse was the smarter way to go. Clear remorse, so I said "sorry," again in a very solemn tone.

"You'd better be. I don't have the space to publish the letters in their entirety, but I'll publish excerpts in the 'Letters to the Editor.' Now, don't you have something you're working on?" He nodded his head toward the door.

"Yeah, I'm going, and hmm . . . thanks, thanks a lot, Guido." I sprang from my chair and almost dropped to my knees to kiss his hairy hand. He would not be publishing the entirety of that epic-length letter and the other red-ink documents, excerpts only. One letter like that would be *Sara's Last Stand.* It would have banished me from the field of respectable journalism, practically before I had earned a shot at it and then I'd have to find another soul-sucking job in Queens.

That evening, when I arrived home, I pulled out the crumpled news article stuffed in my pocket. Smoothed it out on the table to reread it slowly. On paper, it appeared harmless and nothing particularly offensive even though it was incredibly offensive to Mexicans. Just so that I was absolutely clear on the scope of my error, Guido later urged me to visit the Mexican Museum of Intervention, a museum full of artifacts and maps showing all the foreign meddling and plots to overthrow the Mexican government. "France, the U.S.," Guido said, and ticked off the countries, "We don't forget any of the villains in our history."

I shuddered. I could almost see God, dressed in a Mexican tricolor flag, standing in the middle of thunder and lightning, He was flashing the most important of the three Mexican Commandments on the graffiti wall of my brain, "Thou Shalt Not Talk About the Mexican-American War."

"On my day off, I'll go and get rehabilitated," I said aloud. I folded the article, creased it into a paper airplane and sent it off, *wheee!* into the air until it sailed into the abyss of the kitchen wastebasket. If I kept that thing, I was sure it would jinx me as a journalist. I had the code memorized. *Never ask a Mexican about the Mexican-American War. Just don't.*

* * *

Honestly, that war-reporting incident lingered longer than I had expected. So long, in fact, that I had entered into a world of journalist infamy. A bad wind clearly blew through the newsroom afterwards. Some reporters had begun to eye me with suspicion as one of those newborn mice that knew nothing about news and credible sources. Kate and Emma avoided me entirely as if I were some Typhoid Mary of the newsroom. *There she goes. The one who used only one biased source and did no fact-checking.* No one said anything specific to me, but they gave me stink eye and I could just tell what some of them were thinking. *Stay away from her. She'll spread bad joo joo on your stories.* Except for Malena, of course.

And sure enough, it wasn't ten days before another stirring event was thrown on my plate. Guido tracked me down in the newsroom. "Sara, I'm sending you across town to the federal police headquarters to report a big bust."

"As in drugs, er . . . and drug dealers? That's what I just said."

"Great." *Here I go again,* a rookie reporter who doesn't know a bag of marijuana from a bag of maple leaves. "You know I'd rather be covering a book signing or an art opening, don't you?"

"No one else is available, Sara. I don't want to hear any

buts."

"But—"

Guido's eyes flashed.

"I can't believe you're making me do this," I said under my breath.

He might have heard. His flashing eyes turned to fire. "Sara, tell me. What are you doing to repair your hack reputation after writing that stupid war article? After causing me so much *vergüenza* shame?"

We Tortellinis can recognize a hint if there ever was one. It's not like the U.S. and Mexico broke off diplomatic relations over my article or anything, but Guido made it feel that way. My best bet was to keep my mouth shut, head to the police headquarters, and cover the drug bust.

The instant I arrived at the federal police headquarters I experienced a not-so-warm glow. *Los federales* were stationed all around the building, every three feet or so, and two of them at the main entrance. Heavily armed, in black fatigues, with hard-toed boots, bulletproof vests, dark sunglasses, and mouths half covered with black masks. Just a glimpse at the men gave me goose bumps so I avoided eye contact as I passed through the door. Just lifted my press pass around my neck to show them I was supposed to be there. One of them growled, pushed off his mask and clenched his teeth, which made me almost wet my pants and run off in the other direction.

The press conference was held in a room bathed in florescent lights with a cold eerie look. On one side of the room were the suspects in a cordoned area. On the other side was a swarm of reporters and photographers pushing to the front to eye the suspects. I jostled elbows and shoulders to move to the front to see the shackled suspects. A young man and a young woman in blue jeans and white T-shirts stood handcuffed. The press corps stared in silence. I felt embarrassed examining them like this. It reminded me of tourists huddling around the Olmeca stone heads in the anthropology museum. When the police ordered the suspects to move, the boy and the girl shuffled closer to the swarm of reporters, heads down and stopped. "Show us your faces!" an official shouted. They lifted their heads. Silent, somber, resolute. Photographers leaned forward, cameras clicked, and flashbulbs flashed.

As soon as an official began reading aloud a press release, I stopped gaping myself and made little black squiggles all over my steno pad. When he finally paused from reading, I looked up from my notebook. Only then did I notice the loot behind the suspected drug suspects. Bundles of marijuana, covered in plastic wrap, were heaped to the ceiling. On one long table were stacks of bills in neat rubber-banded piles. Fierce-looking guns were lined up in rows on another table. When the press officer rattled off numbers, I jotted down how many kilos of marijuana had been seized. Later, I was told, the confiscated marijuana would be burned.

Before I moved to Mexico, I held the mistaken belief that everyone in the world admired journalists. Well, sort of. I knew that we ranked slightly below Hollywood stars. And way below George Clooney and Leonardo DiCaprio. Even so, the Columbia School of Journalism gave out Academy-like awards to reporters that exposed cover-ups and corruption in the States. But it wasn't like that in Mexico. I had heard stories from other reporters that covering government corruption and drug trafficking exposed them to threats of physical harm or harassment.

Learning this, I was terrifically timid and exercised scary quantities of caution in what I wrote after each event I covered. I probably could have been nominated for the Yellow Badge of Cowardliness if there was such an award. I certainly hoped covering this drug bust was a one-time deal and Guido would allow me to play it safe by sticking to general news stories and not getting all investigative. I had gotten myself into enough trouble over reporting on a war that was over a hundred and sixty years old, let alone reporting on the modern one involving drugs.

* * *

"What's this, Sara?" Guido burst into the newsroom clenching a copy of my drug bust article. "A regurgitated press release? Were you even at the drug bust?"

"Sí, señor. All three dimensions. Why?"

"How is it that I've reread your article—I don't know how many times—and I haven't found a piece of news in it? Tell me! None. It's a press release on throw up."

"It's *not* a press release. It just *sounds* like a press release." I stood up to show him my factual fabulousness, a human recorder par excellence. "Look," I pointed to my paragraph one. "There's the lead. Pointed to paragraph two. "There's the number of kilos of marijuana seized." Paragraph three. "There's all the dirty details. See? Names and ages of the suspects. Where they were caught. Number of guns. All there."

"It's a press release on vomit!" Guido snapped. "That's not news!"

"Okay, I admit it's not a riveting read but it's news."

Tsk-tsk-tsk noises came out of Guido's throat. I was so glad that at that moment, someone called him into his office and he left it at that, banging the newsroom door behind him.

It wasn't easy, using mere words, to describe a drug-related arrest for a newspaper article. I knew my story appeared as dry as burned toast, but it all boiled down to the fact I wasn't going out of my comfort level this time. Imagine me writing what little I knew about drugs. That would be a real mistake. I could just picture the entire population of Mexico writing me letters about what they knew about drugs. And then where would I be? On the next plane back to New York, I was sure of it.

4

Not Dead, Just Napping

M alena tossed a bundle of fresh marigold flowers on my lap in the car and asked me to come to her house for the Day of the Dead.

"Eww . . . They smell really awful," I said, picking them up and holding the bouquet an arm's length away.

"Nothing quite like it— the scent of marigolds," Malena said. "What do you know about the Day of the Dead?"

"It's kind of like Halloween, but gloomier 'cause there's no trick or treating."

Malena snickered. "That's it?"

"Almost, smarty pants," I said, and added, "did you know Halloween is not just for kids? Adults dress up too. We have parties and pig out on chocolate. Want to hear how I dressed up as a banana one year?"

"No. The Day of the Dead is *not* Halloween relocated," Malena said, "what else do you know?"

"Your dead ancestors come back to life?"

"Family members never die here." Malena turned her raspy voice into her know-it-all, Mexicanologist voice. "They just take very long naps."

"You mean when they return from the dead?" Long naps and talking about dead people were a million miles away from Halloween.

"Yes, ma'am." She lit up a cigarette. "You'll see."

I coughed. I hated smoke and she knew it. "Mmm . . . so when you die here, forget about resting in peace?"

"Oh, we rest in peace, all right. Just not all the time."

"I know skulls of sugar and skeletons dance around, too."

"You have to set up a family altar to understand. You'll see. We're going to make an altar for my dad, who passed away five years ago."

I ducked my head back inside the car. Hanging it out the window was my only defense against the smell of smoke and the feeling of about-to-puke from the jerky ride.

I shook my head. We were off the highway and stuck at a light. "So you've never actually been to an offering, have you?"

"Nope. This will be my first."

"Thought so." Malena said, blowing her cigarette smoke out the window, adding her little private fumes to the big public ones. "You know," she continued, "Mexicans aren't afraid of death."

"I'm not, either." Even if I was, I wasn't going to admit it.

"Everybody's got to die," Malena reminded me.

"I *know.*"

"We, Mexicans, remember. When we die, we're never forgotten."

When we arrived at Malena's house, her elderly mom sat on a corner of the couch bent over in a crumple. "Mama." Malena bent down and shouted close to her ear. "Sara's here," Malena shouted again.

She looked up at me in a groggy daze and her mouth crinkled in a smile. "Oh, yes, Sara." She sat up a bit and offered me her bony hand.

I gently took it and gave her a peck on the cheek, following a Mexican custom.

"Malena talks about you all the time." She straightened herself more.

"What has she told you?"

Señora Lupe just smiled.

"Let's set up the altar, Sara," Malena said, "We must have four elements, earth, wind, water and fire.

I hung the paper cut-outs, or papel picado, in front of a small desk. Next, we covered the small desk with a tablecloth. Malena handed me two loaves of bread of the dead and three sugar skulls. While I arranged them on the desk, Malena stuck two candles into glass holders, and lit them. Then she pulled out a small flowerpot with sand and buried a copal incense stick in it. She glanced up at me. "You can fill a glass of water and set it out."

"Right." Filling a glass of tap water for the offering, I spotted the stinky marigolds.

Malena poured a pile of salt into a small bowl and placed it next to the glass of water. Next, she set a giant bottle of tequila, and a leather hat right next to the framed photo of the father.

"What are those things for?"

"You'll see. See that fruit bowl over there? Pick out an orange, a lime, and an apple and put them in a small bowl. Dad's favorites."

Malena explained that the candle represents fire, the fruit is for the Earth, and the paper cut designs, the wind, and the glass of water represents the element of water. The food in the offering is left untouched but is symbolically eaten and drunk by her father's returning spirit. Especially the tequila and the eggy, light sweet bread called the Bread of the Dead or "pan de muerto."

Señora Lupe appeared with a pot of tamales and set them on the table. She glanced my way.

"I'm helping," I said, pointing to the fruit bowl.

She nodded and smiled.

"Sara," Malena said, "Come over here and watch me." She plucked the petals off the marigolds and scattered around her dad's favorite chair. "Do it like just like this," she said, handing me the rest of the marigolds "Make a path from the dining room to the front door." Wow, from the looks of it, Malena was really expecting her father to return from the dead.

Señora Lupe returned to the dining room, with a steaming cup of hot chocolate for me and turned to Malena. "Mi hija, open the tequila, por favor."

We all sat down at the table, me with my hot chocolate and they with their bottle of tequila. "Sara, if you could have a person from your family return from the dead," Señora Lupe softly said, "who would it be?"

"Probably my grandmother."

"Tell us about her," Señora Lupe said, slowly reaching for the bottle of tequila.

"Well, Grandma died when I was seven. I used to live with her, along with my cousin and sister. And to me, it was like she just disappeared one day. I remember crying at school so much that my teacher let me sit on her lap every day during reading time."

"You poor darling," Señora Lupe said. "What a shame to have lost her so young."

"Sure you don't want some?" Malena interrupted, pointing to her shot glass and pouring.

"Positive."

"A tiny shot?" Malena asked.

"No, thanks!" I personally thought tequila tasted like dog saliva. I took a sip of hot chocolate right after she asked me about the tequila to make sure she knew I liked that.

Two hours later, this Day of the Dead ritual was feeling a lot like Jesus' Last Supper hosted by the Catholics. We stared at the dad picture together while Malena and her mom drank more shots of tequila. It was like waiting for him to crawl out of the picture frame.

"How did he die?" I asked, studying the picture of Malena's dad.

"Heart attack."

There was a prolonged silence. "I'm sorry. No warning then?"

"None," Malena said.

"I miss mi viejo, "Señora Lupe said. She smiled sadly. "He

was such a good man."

I looked around the room. So far, no strange winds, no whispers, no rattles, but it was feeling creepier and creepier.

"Let's eat," Malena finally said.

"Yes, let's!" I shouted on a wave of relief.

We devoured platters of homemade chicken mole, beans, rice and tamales. Then we prayed I don't know how many "Hail Mary's" and a whole lot of "Our Fathers." All in Spanish —so they were a lot longer. As Malena and her mother drank more shots of tequila, I was thinking nobody had told me that the Day of the Dead was supposed to be a celebration of drinking, eating, praying and then more drinking.

After Señora Lupe said goodnight, and went to bed, Malena and me were left to wait for her father's return. I squirmed in my seat to escape the stink of those awful marigolds.

Malena didn't take the hint when I kept looking at my watch so I finally said, "It's getting late."

"You aren't dreaming of going to bed at ten o'clock, are you?"

I stifled my yawn. "Heck, no."

As the night groaned on, Malena suddenly stood up, gripped the empty tequila bottle, pointed to the label and announced. "Sara, welcome, Tequila." She looked at the bottle and then back at me with a dramatic wave of her hand. "Blue Agave, this is Sara." Then she looked at me expectantly. "Say something."

"Um, Malena?" I said softly. "I believe you've uncorked yourself like that bottle you're holding."

"Say nice to meet you, Sara. It's waiting for your polite greeting." Her finger jabbed at the label *Tequila Añejo*.

"Malena. Sorry, ahm . . . I think it's time to go to bed."

"You know that guy, what'shisname, um . . .Paz! Yes, that's it! Octavio Paz said, 'Tell me how you die and I'll tell you who you are.' Or is it tell me who you are and I'll tell you how you die? Well, anyway, something like that . . . I mean, if whatchamalcallit says it or said it. The fellow is dead now, I think, but not sure. Anyway, like youknowhoimean says, he should know. I mean, about death." She sat down. "I'm not tired and I'm not going to bed."

"You're not?" I closed my eyes to rest them.

"You're not going to sleep on me, are you Sara?" Malena asked.

"Nah, I can think better with my eyes closed, that's all." My eyelids stayed shut.

"Is somebody there? Hello?" Malena's voice rising. My eyes popped open. "Hello?" Malena said again. "I'm feeling something, Sara."

"*What?*"

"I feel his vibration. I see him. He's here." There was a look of awe in her eyes. "Sitting in that chair. Dressed in a black suit. "He's saying hello. Do you hear him?"

"Who?"

"My *dad*." Her face filled with joy. Can't you see him, Sara? He's sitting in his favorite chair."

Spinning around, I checked all around me. "Where?" I shrilled. "I can't see him."

"In front of you! In his chair, I said!"

I rubbed my eyes hard and scanned the room from top to bottom. "Nope, nothing."

"Oh, Papa, I have something that's been weighing on my heart." She swallowed hard. "I have been having an affair with Guido."

Oh, my God! I wish I could have heard her dad's side of the conversation. One thing I knew. I can't imagine talking about my love life to my father. She must have been really close to her father to do that.

"It has been going on a long time, Papa," she exhaled in relief. "I'm sorry, Papa. Will you forgive me?"

Malena bowed her head. "Thank you for forgiving me, Papa." Thank you for giving me your blessing! I miss you! Goodbye, Papa." She looked around with tears rolling down her cheek.

The Spirit Dad must have disappeared. I cleared my throat. "An affair with Guido? Our boss? *Panzón*, big belly Guido?"

"*That* Guido." Malena wiped her eyes. "It just kind of happened. A couple of years ago. And it keeps stretches on and on."

"What do you mean?"

Her eyes filled with fear. "Now I want you, Sara Tortellini, to forget all about it. Forget that I told you."

"I won't utter a syllable about your affair with the *panzón*. Promise."

I had to admit a sense of relief washed over me when Malena stood up, teeter-tottered in the direction of her bedroom, mumbling, "*Um*, we *er*, should go, *um* to bed."

I headed for the guest bedroom and fell asleep immediately.

The next morning, in the post-tequila, post-confessional era, Malena appeared as normal as could be. No signs of suffering from a headache, or a hangover, and she was in her sixties.

"You sure are quiet," Malena remarked as she drove me home.

"Well, I'm thinking." She didn't need to know about my bad headache.

"I like you quiet."

"Ha ha. Was that supposed to be funny?"

5

Starstruck

I finally found a new place to live. Smack dab in the center of town, on a street called Isabel La Católica. When someone asked, I told them I lived in a prehistoric complex next to the Aztec ruins. In a set of buildings that suffered from a bad case of rheumatoid arthritis in their stones and mortar. Every day, on my way to work, I caught these centuries-old buildings groaning about their fault lines and comparing their rates of sinkage. Despite the aging complex, I was thrilled with my new habitat. I wasn't alone anymore when I came home, either. I shared an indoor central patio with all eight of my Mexican neighbors, who welcomed me into their neighborhood, called *una vecindad*.

No more Drunk Husband pounding at my door and bawling like a baby. No more pillows for ear buds. No more nights hiding under my bed. After my first apartment ordeal, I was ready to form a hand-holding circle and wish for peace, harmony and goodwill toward all women, especially all ex-wives and ex-lovers.

Oh, there were adjustments to make. Like no indoor heat. As the sun melted into the horizon, my place became naturally climate controlled. I went to bed equipped to sleep in an igloo: thick tights, fluffy socks and a baggy sweatshirt.

My morning showers changed, too. They went from a few snappy minutes of tap dancing to an advanced ballet performance. When my alarm rang, the first thing I'd do is poke my head from under the blankets and puff. I'd wait to see if my breath turned to fog. If I did, I shrugged and told myself, "*ni modo*," Oh, well! There was nothing I could do about it. Even a cloud-breathing dragon had to get clean.

Whenever I was in the mood to moan about my new daily regime, I consoled myself with the fact my new career as a reporter at *The Observer* had grown so intense that I wasn't home all that much. I was putting in ten to twelve-hour days. When I came back to my place, I could have fallen asleep on ping pong balls.

Alex was so loyal as a cousin and kept in touch with me when I'd call him about those nightly visits of the Drunk Husband in my last apartment. As soon as I moved into my new place, he phoned to see if I was doing okay. "How's your Spanish coming along?" he asked. "The last time we talked, you told me you were having a hard time at the press conferences. Is that any better?"

"Not really. I still have trouble understanding abstract concepts or academic vocabulary. It doesn't help that I have my self-esteem the size of a pinto bean."

"Oh, you'll get the hang of it. I know you will. You have the Tortellini toughness."

I sure hoped Alex was right.

* * *

Not long after moving into my new place, Guido sent me to my first literary conference. Where all the presenters were famous authors and professors of literature. Walking into the auditorium and scanning for an empty seat, my eyes settled on a man wearing a simple brown sweater with bushy, bushy eyebrows furrowed in deep concentration. Geez, he looked familiar. Where do I know him from? I stared at him again. In fact, he looked kind of famous. Was that . . . no, it couldn't be, could it? No paparazzi crawled on their knees in the aisle, blinding him with glaring lights. No fellow reporters were shoving their recorders in his face. I studied him some more. Was it? Then a tingle ran down to my toes. It had to be. His thick horn-rimmed glasses and a fuzzy mustache gave him away. He looked exactly like the photo of him on the back cover of his best seller, *One Hundred Years of Happiness*. And *exactly* like Marcelo had described him. It *had* to be him.

The Miguel Hernández. The literary star of the Spanish-speaking world.

The most important human being I have seen. Ever.

(The famous Batman guy I met in person for naming the movie title on the radio station didn't count. I didn't even like the movie, *Batman*.)

I sat on the edge of my seat. Not any seat, mind you. A seat exactly three rows and two seats over from *Him*. Since I was on assignment, had a deadline and a literary conference to cover, I reluctantly fished out my notebook and pen and tried to concentrate on the speaker presenting, listening hard.

My ear detected a *teedah-teedah-teedah*. What was he saying? Formal, academic vocabulary. This was bad. Why was he was talking so fast? It sounded like one run-on sentence. I waited for him to gulp for air. He needed no air.

This was really bad. I needed air. And English subtitles.

Most of all, I needed a story. I panicked. The level of academic Spanish used in the presenter's speech was too complex for me to catch. The next presenter's speech was even worse. Too abstract. I had a certain number of newsprint inches to fill so I took a few notes about where the place was located, estimated the number of seats in the auditorium and tried to figure out what else I should do. Should I turn in a muddled non-report or worse, nothing at all? I decided neither.

With such an important literary conference, there had to be a stenographer lurking somewhere to produce a transcript of what these important presenters were saying. I would run to the transcript department as soon as the conference was done. Meanwhile, I needed to introduce myself to Miguel Hernandez, the one and only.

The audience was still applauding when I stood up. I was all set to rub elbows with *The Miguel Hernández*. Clutching a notebook of cramped, illegible notes, I made my way to *Him*, and tried not to appear like a swooning fan. With each step closer to him, I thought that I really wanted to make a good impression, not like a literary lowlife gushing with fan *oohs* and *ahs*. I'll be completely composed, extend a beautiful handshake, use eloquent words, and tell him how much I admire his work, reveal my favorite novel, and then I will ask him for his autograph. Even if he has to sign the cover of my notebook.

As I marched closer, the cords of my neck tightened and the word *chicken* kept popping up. Try role reversal Sara. Pretend he's an ant, and you are The Jolly Green Giant. There's nothing to be afraid of. *Go.*

When I said "go" in my head, Hernández stood up and moved to the end of his row. At that moment, I reached the end of his row too. Perfect. Perfect meeting of literary minds. *Now, introduce yourself, idiot.* Ask for his autograph. I opened my mouth but nothing came out.

Just drool.

Hernández smiled. He had a mysterious aura about him. His smile glowed like a halo.

I brushed up against him while he stood at the edge of the aisle, hoping his fame would fall on me like literary dandruff. Still no words. Not even a syllable. I didn't even say a *"disculpe"* an "excuse me" as I swept past him with my mouth gaping like an idiot.

Drool.

By the time I reached the woman at the transcript window, I felt as if I had inhaled large doses of nitrous oxide. When I finally let go of the tension, I had a bad case of the giggles. Uncontrollable *hee-hees*. The stenographer peeked at me through a pair of glasses lowered on her nose. "How can I help you?"

I stifled my giggles for a few seconds. When I opened my mouth, something came out all weird: "Today see star Hernandez Miguel Nobel famous let's autograph ourselves together I write no much. Handshake. That is. OK?"

"Excuse me, Señorita?" the transcript lady said.

My giggling erupted again while trying to make complete sentences. "Hee-hee . . . do you know who I bumped into? Hernández! *The* Miguel Hernández! I was this close to getting his autograph."

She leaned back away from me. "This is the transcript office."

Oh, I could see she was annoyed.

Stone-faced.

Giggles stopped.

"Are you here for a transcript?"

"Yes, I need the transcript, *desperately*."

"The conference has just ended. You'll have to come back at five o'clock."

"Uh, you see, I have a deadline . . ."

"Five o'clock. That's all I can do."

"But I need it before five to meet my deadline." I glanced at my watch. It was three o'clock. "You see, I'm from *The Observer*, it's a tiny newspaper that practically nobody reads. I mean, besides foreigners and the government censorship committee. And as if you can't tell already, Spanish is a foreign language, I mean my foreign language—"

"Sorry, five o'clock, and if you excuse me, I need to get back to my work." The transcript lady whirled around, strutted across the floor and disappeared into the back, leaving an empty office behind her.

I hit my head against the wall lightly, then slid slowly to the floor. I blew it! Now, I couldn't tell anyone that I had actually *met* Hernández. I could only say I *saw* the literary giant or that I *bumped into* him, the Nobel Prize winner. I could hear it all now. The sophisticated conversation opener:

"Hey, you know Miguel Hernández?"

"Of course, why?"

"I shared an *auditorium* with him."

Two reporters from the Mexican dailies, *El Universal* and *La Jornada*, turned up a few minutes later, all fresh-faced. "We're here to get a transcript. Man, that was heavy-duty stuff, wasn't it? Did you see Hernández in there? I actually got to tell him how much I admired his work. He told me it took seven years to finish his last book."

The other fellow reporter waved the conference program in the air, "I got his autograph!"

"Let me see it." I glanced at Hernandez' autograph to see if was true. His conference booklet was covered with a scrawl that read Miguel Hernandez. "Good for you."

"What about you?" he asked.

I shook my head. "A terrible, terrible thing happened to me in there."

"In there?" He pointed to the auditorium.

I nodded. "I became Starstuck," I said in English. "I mean Star*suck*."

"*What?*" the reporter asked.

"Don't mind me," I told the reporters and waved him off.

One of them poked his head through the window. "Hello? Anybody here?" But no one answered. The Mexican reporters waited until four-thirty, when both of them left. Meanwhile, I called Guido to tell him I was held up in the transcript department and to keep the ten-inch space in the newspaper for me.

The stenographer emerged three minutes before five o'clock with a pile of very smudged photocopies. "Here you are," she said as she pointed at the office clock, "it's even before five o'clock."

"Oh, thank you, thank you, very kind of you," I said, flipping through the pages.

A faint smile spread across her face as she patted me on the shoulder. "I could tell you really needed those documents."

"Oh, yes, I did!" Wait, how could she tell? Oh, never mind. Time to get out of here.

I made a mad dash out of the theater, racing around the

corners of the itty-bitty streets again, turning right, right again, then turning left, through a courtyard, down some steps, and another right until I ran into a cluster of people sitting on red plastic overturned buckets. They were listening to a voice booming from giant speakers set out on the street. *"Grey! Pink!* Repeat after me! The students roared back: *"Grey! Pink!* She is wearing *grey* pants. Her blouse is *pink."* What do you know, it was an outdoor English lesson. I needed a lesson like this, I thought, but in Spanish, so I could understand what was being said at that conference. I didn't stop, though. It was full speed ahead to *The Observer* with a promise to myself that I would get Spanish tutoring very soon.

That evening, I found Malena in the newsroom examining three enlarged photos spread over three desks. She said without looking up from her photographs. "I can't talk to you now, Sara. Have to finish this. I'm checking the spelling of the names of these guests . . . from a cocktail party I went to last night."

"Well, not to brag or anything, but guess who I bumped into this afternoon?"

"Can't talk right now." She picked up a photograph.

"You won't believe who I saw."

"I told you. Have to finish this."

"Somebody famous. A *celebrity."*

"Who? No, let me guess. The president of the United States who came to talk about immigration again?"

"Nope. *The* Miguel Hernández," I announced.

Malena stopped fingering her photos. "You saw him? Where?"

"At a literary conference."

She looked up. "Did you get his autograph?"

"No."

Her eyes widened. "You get a picture with him?"

"No."

Her eyebrows shot up. "A handshake?"

I shook my head.

"Not even a handshake?" Malena's voice rose an octave

higher from her normally low rasp. "You didn't even get a handshake?"

"Okay, stop it."

"You were that close to him, and you said nothing? Ha-ha." Her cackle was almost demonic.

"I just froze up."

"*Chica*, you stick around Malena more and I'll teach you a bit about celebrity sightings."

* * *

After that conference, I stuck little yellow sticky Post-it notes all around my apartment, on the bathroom mirror, on the refrigerator door, and even on my lampshades. They all read FIND Spanish tutor ASAP. No excuses. I tried hard to ignore the notes but when I read them, I muttered to myself, "I will, I will, I will."

The need for a tutor turned more critical after I ran into Enrique's wife and kids when they stopped by the newsroom to bring him lunch. I didn't mean to eavesdrop or anything, but I noticed Enrique's wife was calling their three-year-old son papito or daddy even though his name was Pablo. You see, right off the bat, I picked up on how nicknames lacked any logic. My ear espionage caught Enrique's wife calling their daughter mamita or mommy even though the daughter was nursery school age and named Beatriz. Getting Enrique to explain, I uncovered more nicknames. Enrique calls his mother mi jefa, my boss, and his wife mi vieja, my old lady.

Hearing this, I concluded: nicknames in Mexico were based on some weird family dynamics. By using reverse psychology, Mexicans code the real name of the person to clandestinely communicate with family members. Assuming nicknames were only for family members, I saw no reason to worry about acquiring one. "Right, Enrique?" I asked him after his wife and kids had left.

"No, that's not the way it works. We call our kids papi and mami as a way to say sweet words like honey and dear in

English. As for nicknames, Mexicans give nicknames to friends and foes alike."

"What do you mean?"

"To someone like you."

Uh-oh. "You mean someone outside the family gene pool?"

"Sure."

"Friend or foe?"

"Friend of course."

"Well how exactly do make one?"

"Simple. We find a trait that stands out in the person. A strange physical or personality trait. Then we create a nickname to make fun of it. Simple as that."

"Simple as that, huh?" My eyes narrowed on Enrique, my hands firmly planted on my hips. "You're not planning to give me one, are you, Enrique?"

"Ha, ha!" he said.

"Ha, ha!" I said back. "You better not."

"Don't worry."

Which, of course, failed to reassure me. At any moment, with my luck, I'll be baptized "Big Mouth," or *Hocicona* for my big mouth, or *China* for my curly hair, or even *Decimal,* a decimal point for the huge beauty mark on my chin. I just knew it. I was just waiting for it to happen.

A couple of weeks passed. Thank God, my colleagues continued to call me Sara here and Sara there. Just when I was on the verge of being nicknameless, Carlos and Felix, the newspaper office boys, whizzed by with a cup of steaming coffee for me and a bundle of the mail. "*Hola, morena linda.*"

"*Morena?*" I asked them.

"*Sí, morena.* We call you *morena, con cariño.*"

How sweet, I thought. They called me dark-skinned with affection. "Pretty dark skinned." Wait a minute. Did they say *morena? Dark-skinned?* Why were they doing that? My skin tone was *olive.* The color of an army uniform. Not pale as light bulb to make it ironic. Not deep espresso. Medium Olive. And "dark-skinned," or "little darkie," or "pretty dark skinned" was definitely *not* funny.

This was serious. Maybe Mexicans didn't realize that calling someone darkie in the U.S. would be considered a huge mistake. How racist it sounded, how much legal trouble you could get in. But I wasn't in New York or anywhere close to the U.S. I was in Mexico. So I told myself that the best way to handle this not-so-funny and not-so-nice nickname was to develop a thick skin. Act like it was no big deal. Be strong. I chanted *Mexico is not for the meek and mild. Mexico is not for the meek and mild. Mexico is not for the meek and mild.*

So that was what I did. I wore my durable skin when my *morena* nickname spread like a California wildfire in the newsroom. Soon my fellow reporters stopped calling me Sara this or Sara that, and began calling me *morena. Morena?* No problem. I did not and would not pay attention to it.

Weeks blew by for "the little darkie." Then, as I lingered by the mail basket, waiting patiently for the daily bundle of mail and hoping Alex would remember me with a package from New York, Carlos cruised by. He dumped a pile of envelopes in the basket, gave me a glimpse and whistled through his lips. "*Morena,* where did you hide your crown?"

"What do you mean?"

"Your crown, *mi reina?*"

My crown? What crown? *Wait a minute.* Crown, did you say?

"*Sí, la corona para una reina.* Crown for a queen.

It suddenly dawned on me that I'd been hearing my nickname wrong all along. Not *morena,* little darkie. *Mi reina,* my queen.

"Hah-hah. You were calling me queen all this time? You mean the opposite of King, right?"

"*Sí, mi reina.* Don't get mad."

Mad? Oh, no. Who could be mad? I burst out laughing. Embarrassed, yes. Mad, no. How could I be? I was a drama queen all right. The Queen of Tin Ears. No, I was the Queen of the Broken Hearts who came down to Mexico to fix the major love organ but had suddenly inherited a crown of jewels. I couldn't detect the difference between the vowel "o" and "i", or the distinction between *morena* and *mi reina.* My ears needed wax removal or serious training in Spanish. I was planning to do something to improve my listening comprehension and to mend my heart faster. I just hadn't figured out what it would be.

Then I remembered all those yellow sticky notes I had plastered all over my apartment to find a tutor. It was hard enough living like a Mexican, but speaking like one was next to impossible. First the conference. Then that whole nickname business had sent me over the brink.

My ear needed real work.

6

How to Speak Mexican Fluently

However humiliating, (I mean, after all, I did very well on that translation test when I first interviewed for the job), and however expensive, (I was always peso-pinching), and however painful (I wanted to minimize memorization), I swallowed the lump in my throat and called the Department of Linguistics at Mexico's National Autonomous University. Did they know a highly respected phlebotomist who drew blood so I could learn Spanish by blood transfusion?

That is how I met Francisco, a fourth-year linguistics student. Over the phone, we agreed on a Struggle Exchange. Since I was struggling with Spanish and he was struggling to raise his score on the Graduate Record Exam in order to study in the States, we reached a deal. *Hecho*. Done.

The following day Francisco showed up at my house for my first lesson, and told me right away that there was no way of transferring Spanish words into my blood intravenously.

"I didn't think so, but thought I'd try," I told him. By his voice on the phone, I had pictured him nerdy, with thick glasses and no social graces, but he wasn't like that at all. He was thin as a sheet of loose-leaf paper and his face had chiseled features framed by a mass of unruly brown hair. He greeted me with a hearty handshake, more like Americans like to do, followed by a formal *Buenos Dias*, like Mexicans do. This gave me the impression that he was bicultural from the start. His courteous manners and his youngish looks made him charming despite his big ears that stuck out like the handles of the World Cup trophy.

To start, I told him the most important thing. "Besides all the academic and formal vocabulary, I want to learn, I really want to blend in. Maybe teach me some slang. Sound more Mexican. Less *gringa*."

"Okay, we'll start with how to make a basic telephone call."

"Phone call?"

"Yes."

Talk about ego busting, we were going to role-play a phone call?

"First of all, Mexicans answer the phone with *Bueno*," he began.

"Good?"

"Yes, good."

"Forget the ¡*Hola!* I learned from Sr. Gomez?"

"Right."

Francisco continued. "When you don't understand what they are saying on the other end, you say ¿*Mande*? Got it? You ask this in a question kind of lilt, which means, "Order me!"

"But the dictionary says—"

"Swallow your dictionary. That's what we use here."

"I get it, but what happened to the ¿*Cómo*? I learned in Spanish class?"

"That works here, but they'll know you aren't Mexican. You said you wanted to blend in, didn't you? Sound more Mexican, didn't you?"

"You're right." I was pretty sure at this point Francisco would reverse our barter arrangement and charge me triple his normal tutoring rate.

For the second lesson, Francisco taught me some Mexican slang. I learned that ¡*Híjole!* ("Oh, my Gosh!") has nothing to do with a son, (*hijo*) ¡*Ándale*! ("Go aahead!") has nothing to do with walking (*andar*) and ¡*Órale*! ("Okay!") has nothing to do with praying (*orar*) despite the way the words look and sound.

"When can I use these words?" I asked.

"When you want to show shock, surprise, and encouragement. It can mean "Oh, my Gosh!" or "Go ahead!" or just an ordinary "Okay!"

"Wait, let me write all these words down." I scribbled furiously. I was so excited about picking up this new local lingo. The slang I needed to fit in. "Wait, you're telling me—"

"—To throw your dictionary in the mud."

As soon as he left, I began hurling the Mexican Spanish equivalents of "Oh, my Gosh," and "Okay," and "Go ahead" as much as I could to anyone who would listen to see if more Mexicans understood me and surprisingly, they did. Even if they were only mild expressions of surprise, they sounded much nastier to me.

Oh, I couldn't wait for each new lesson.

Week by week, we chipped away at my layers of ignorance. Three months went by and we sat at my kitchen table for another Spanish lesson when Francisco announced, "Today, we will learn how to use diminutives and augmentatives."

"Great," I said, my pencil sharpened, even though I didn't know what he was talking about. What on earth were diminutives and augmentatives? I had been reduced to riding a bike with training wheels.

Francisco explained. "These endings we stick onto words, for example, you add -*ito* to *rato* to make things appear smaller, changing the phrase "a little while," "*un rato*" into "*un ratito*." Or add an augmentative ending such as -*zon* or –*ote* to words makes words bigger and badder."

"Oh, making things bigger and badder sounds like a lot more fun than making things small and cutesy."

"Oh, it is. You can call someone with a big nose a *narizón*, or some guy with big belly, a *panzón*."

"You don't dare call them this to their face, do you?" I wondered if his big ears were fair game.

"It depends. Here in Mexico, we are not so worried about being politically correct. We call people we know all kinds of names without really offending them. They function kind of like nicknames."

"Oh, I'm familiar with nicknames. Actually, I'm feeling kind of like an expert at nicknames." Little did he know, but he was already *Orejón* (Big Ears) to me.

"So if I see someone with huge hands, I could say, that is, if he is a friend, that he has *las manos grandotes?*"

"Right!" Francisco beamed and clapped his hands.

Francisco's excitement at understanding such a basic concept of diminutives and augmentatives made me feel embarrassed. After such praise, I concluded that learning a foreign language was akin to reducing myself to a three-year-old. It was like saying toilet correctly for the first time and having my parents give me a Barney sticker for it.

The lesson went on. Francisco gazed at me longer and longer as the lesson progressed. I wasn't falling for my tutor, really, it was just that during this lesson, I was dangling my legs and Francisco was kicking my feet with his feet below the kitchen table. Hard to concentrate on Spanish endings when under the table someone was fooling around with the feet.

When his playful footsies had turned into a prolonged pressing of his leg against mine, I panicked. Was this significant? It was time to turn our kindergarten play into an adult conversation. I was drumming up enough courage to talk to him about it but he kept going on about these silly augmentatives before he suddenly stopped. "Do you know what I like about you?"

"Um, no." I swallowed hard. I was hoping it wasn't something like the way I cover up my thick calves with long dresses.

"Your pretty hands." He reached across the kitchen table and took my hand in his slender fingers with bitten nails, lightly rubbed his lips against my palm and then kissed it.

I pulled my hand away. "That tickles."

"See what I mean?"

"What?"

"Your hands are absolutely magic." Then he reached for my palm again and drew it to his face and rubbed it against his cheek. He was breathing heavily and murmuring in a dreamy voice. "Absolutely magic."

I jerked my hand back. "Um, Francisco, I've been meaning to talk to you about what's going on between us. I ran my fingers through my hair. "I mean, there isn't anything but if there is anything between us, we need to discuss it, I mean, if you have a girlfriend or wife?"

"Neither of those."

"I'm really too old to get involved with someone, uh, that's—"

"Twenty-two? I'm twenty-two."

"Right. Twenty-two." I cleared my throat. My words weighed twenty-two pounds each. "That's um, *almost* eight years younger. That wouldn't work. You see? Uh, that's not what the problem really is. Actually, what the problem is . . . is kind of complicated."

"Shh." He gently put a finger to my lips and touched my hair.

I held up my palms in defensive mode. "No, Francisco, I can't. Um, for now, let's keep it student and tutor. We can just be just friends, can't we? I really need to keep it to Spanish."

"You don't even give me a chance, do you?"

"A boyfriend complicates things."

"Okay, if that's what you want, that's what you want, for now." He returned to his side of the table and started tossing his books in his bag. "I have to go. Study page 29 on the diminutives and augmentatives for next week's review."

"No more footsies, right?" I asked as he turned to leave.

"Done with the footsies. *Hasta la próxima.* See you next time."

Bye, *Orejón.* Big Ears. I didn't call him big ears aloud, of course.

I shut the door and let out a sigh of relief. Wow. Someone had finally expressed interest in me again. For the first time, a guy had tried to climb through the spiky cactus needles that poked men around me away. Stay away from me was my message. Let me live my life as a cactus.

Then again, he's a twenty-two-year-old guy. Maybe all he wanted to do is get naked and have sex. Silly me, thinking he wanted to build a relationship. Too risky when I was still confused. Anyway, I sent him a clear message. He was too young. Still in college. Are you kidding? College was centuries away from my world. Besides, when I wasn't working, I liked being by myself, even if I had been a bit lonely at times.

Our next Spanish lesson suffered a few awkward moments. We were preparing for his GRE exam this time and afterwards, we would do a short lesson in Spanish. I didn't know if I should apologize but decided against it. I was honest. We went through the Verbal Reasoning section of the GRE. When Francisco caught my eye, I looked away. We even managed to get into a student and tutor mode at one point. He was circling something in the reading text when I asked if he wanted some coffee, "*¿Quieres un cafecito?*"

"See? You're sounding more Mexican by the day," he told me. "Sure."

I brought two steaming mugs of Nescafe.

"You just used diminutives correctly and in context."

"I did?"

"Okay, it's your turn for a Spanish lesson." He shifted in his chair and looked at me with anticipation. "Today, I will teach you the all-important, easy-to-pronounce, and very Mexican word: *ahorita*. It means a little now."

"A little now?"

"It can also mean "wait a minute," or "he'll be here in another hour or so," or "you can check back tomorrow.""

"Wait, it can't mean all those things?"

He nodded. "It just depends."

"On what?"

"What the person wants to say."

"You're kidding, aren't you? You don't expect me to be a Mexican mind reader, do you?" Clearly something wasn't right.

"*Ahorita* is just a word we use when we aren't sure how long a wait will be. We have a hunch, though, that it will be soon."

"Hunch? What about an agenda? Or a watch? Isn't that what schedules are for?"

Francisco shrugged. "That's just the way it is. We're kind of flexible with time in Mexico."

"Weasel word," I wrote in my notebook, and then under it the word, *ahorita.*"

Francisco grabbed my hand to bend my fingers the proper way to show me the gesture that accompanies the little now expression. I held my thumb and forefinger about a half inch apart opened my mouth wide to say *ahorita.*

I practiced what Francisco taught me. *Ahorita. Ahorita. Ahorita.*

"Now be careful with the pronunciation. You don't pronounce the letter 'h,' remember?"

In order to avoid being crowned the Miss Pronunciation of Mexico, I decided to practice even more. "*Ahorita. Ahorita. Ahorita,*"

"You got it," Francisco said. "No 'h.' It sounds like *arita.*"

"*Ahorita? Ahorita? Ahorita?*" I continued. *Ahorita. Ahorita. Ahorita.* "Why can't I hear the 'o' in it, either?"

"That's okay. You can stop now."

I stopped saying that cutesy word, feeling a bit smug. "Will you let me out early for good behavior?"

Francisco wasn't done describing the nuances of how Mexicans use time. I listened to him carefully, and when he was through, I was convinced that Albert Einstein had been living in Mexico when he developed his Theory of Relativity. Francisco sat there patiently as I wrote feverishly in a spiral notebook about the physics of Mexican time.

Mexicanly Things to Know About Time

1. **"*ahorita*"** (a little now)—An undetermined amount of time. (seconds-minutes-hours-days). Like waiting for the light in order to cross the street. You know it's coming but you have

no idea when.

2. **"en *5 minutos*"** (in 5 minutes)—An undetermined amount of time.

(hours-a day). Similar to the feeling of waiting in line to renew your registration at the Department of Motor Vehicles, usually longer than an *"ahorita"*.

3. **"*en un ratito*"** (a little while)—An undetermined amount of time.

(hours-days). You point toward the west where the sun sets. You hope it's not too many sunsets, usually longer than *"en 5 minutos."*

4. **"*dentro de poco*"** (a little while)—An undetermined amount of

time. (hours-days-weeks). Like watching a flower bloom, usually longer than *"en un ratito."*

5. **"*mañana*"** (tomorrow)—An undetermined amount of time

(months-years). There's a possibility that it might not happen in this lifetime, usually longer than *"dentro de poco."*

Of all beautiful timekeeping words that Mexicans hold dear, Francisco stressed, *"ahorita"* truly remained the dearest and the most difficult word of the time expressions to master. It ran far ahead of *"un ratito"* and *"dentro de poco."*

Wouldn't you know it, after that lesson with Francisco, I bumped into someone actually using the word *ahorita*.

I had set up an interview with an economics professor, Professor Piña, rather successfully, I might add, following my Franciso's advice on proper phone etiquette. I emerged from the elevator on the fifth floor and was greeted by an administrative assistant. After small talk about the beautiful office high-rise and the traffic, she told me to have a seat. I had just arrived and felt rather hyper so "having a seat" was the last thing I wanted to do. I paced around the lobby a bit. When several minutes went by and there was no sign of Professor Piña, the secretary behind the desk reassured he would, indeed, come. "When do you expect him?"

"*Ahorita*," she said and held up her thumb and forefinger about an inch apart to show me "the little now."

There it was! That catch-all word, *ahorita*. Now how to figure out how much time that was? I was on my own now.

The secretary motioned for me to sit down in one of those chairs in the lobby to wait.

Oh great, I muttered. How long will this *ahorita* be? Was this "little now" going to be a short one or a long one? Was Professor Piña parking his car downstairs or was I going to have to return the next day? I was sure Einstein must have come up with his theory of relativity right here.

The clock ticks at a different pace in Mexico. So I waited and waited and waited.

The magic ticking away of time in Mexico. Breathing deeply, I convinced myself that this was a good test to strengthen my patience, to be in the Zen moment of "the (little) now." I studied the palms of my hands, tracing the lines, wondering which line revealed my lifespan, which one was my love line. For the lifespan line, I knew Marcelo had shortened that line by at least nine years. And what was the meaning of the line which ran halfway down my wrist? I turned my palms over, glanced at my watch, and looked up. "Do you know if he is on his way?" I asked in my sweetest voice.

She gave me a wide plastic grin, "*Un ratito.*"

Oh, great. The "little now" had turned into a "a little while" *un ratito*. Another diminutive that Francisco had taught me. Was this significant? Yes. Wasn't that a little longer than the little now?

Minutes accumulated. *Tick. Tick. Tick.* The magic ticking away of time.

The secretary called the professor to see if he was on his way but there was no answer.

I waited for 30 minutes in real time. Which roughly worked

out to 30 weeks with my sense of time.

In 30 weeks:

I dug out the Copper Canyon with a spoon.

I counted every imagined stone on the street.

I served two life sentences in jail.

I walked around the world three times.

In real life:

I became an expert on killing time in the bathroom.

I went through three coats of lipstick, wiping each one slowly off before meticulously applying another coat.

I studied the big hand and the little hand on the clock hanging on the wall.

I even twiddled my thumbs.

After making a significant number of paces down the lobby again, I returned to sitting down before springing out of my seat to ask one more time, "Do you know how much longer he will be?"

This time the administrative assistant's smile vanished. Through gritted teeth, she hissed *"ahorita."* I was positive she was relishing saying that word over and over again to me.

"Ahorita. Ahorita. Ahorita." I repeated under my breath and sank in my chair again.

All I could do was gnash my teeth as minutes limped by. I had been warned that upsetting an administrative assistant would get me absolutely nowhere. I reminded myself that people in Mexico take it all in stride. They say, "Mexicans arrive on time for only two events—funerals and bullfights." They never rant and rave if another person fails to show up or is late.

When it hit forty-five minutes past the appointment, I had progressed into putting people in categories. Those who wait and those make others wait. *The waiters* and *the waitees*, if you will. Sara was the *waiter*. And Sara was done waiting for Professor Piña, *the waitee*. When the *waiter* waits forty-five minutes for a *waitee*, it should be accepted, in my opinion, as a declaration of war.

At this point, I stood up.

"He'll be coming," the receptionist repeated. This time her

smile was clearly fake and I knew what she really wanted to do was twist my neck off.

Hearing this, things became even more strained as I said, "I'm sorry, but I can't wait for him any longer."

I darted into the elevator and smashed the FIRST FLOOR. As I was bouncing down to the lobby, I thought I was learning how to be more patient in Mexico but not *that* patient. I wasn't the Joan of Arc of Patience or anything. It was hopeless. I would never be able to wait in a calm, resigned manner like a Mexican, no matter how long I lived here.

The doors opened and I tore out of the elevator.

"Sara?" A bespectacled jovial man in the lobby rushed up to me as I was making a mad dash toward the exit.

"Yes?"

"Professor Piña. *Encantado.*"

I blinked.

"So sorry I kept you waiting. Traffic was horrible. Are you still up to having our meeting today?"

You mean am I still up to being alive? My thoughts turned to Guido. He was going to barbecue me if I refused to return for Professor Piña's interview. I gulped for some air, and swallowed my pride before stepping inside the elevator. "Sure."

"I was hoping so. Great!"

"No, no, after *you!*" Professor Piña said. We shot straight up back to the fifth floor. Oh, wouldn't the administrative assistant be thrilled to see me again.

The doors of the elevator slid open and there she sat. The second she eyeballed me, she let out a very long *"¡Híjoleeeeee!"* Her utterance of shock, equivalent to "Oh, my goshhhhhhhh!)" was a total turnaround from her composed, plastic self. Still, it was better than the expected nasty, *"You, again?"*

"Have you already met Sara Tortellini?" the professor asked.

After she closed her mouth, she nodded. Then turning to me, she secretly made a face that could skewer a few limbs of mine on a meat hook. "Oh, yes. We know each other—"

"Very, very, very well," I finished her sentence. "Don't we?"

Not only that. For the very first time, I understood her utterance of shock. Her stretched out "oh-my-gosh" ness was perfectly clear. Mexican slang. One small step for Sara, one giant leap for the ear.

7

A Glimpse of the Virgin

W hen my city editor Enrique stopped pecking at his computer keys to suddenly peer above his glasses at me and ask, "Have you visited the Virgin yet?" I looked up from the story I was writing and even though I knew what he was talking about, I asked, "What Virgin?"

"The shrine for the Virgin of Guadalupe, of course."

"You can't live in this city without visiting the Virgin," Enrique went on. "Visiting the Virgin is very Mexican. As Mexican as molé."

"I know. I just don't know when I'll get the time." I returned to tapping away at my story.

The Virgin was a celebrity here. Jesus was popular here in Mexico like the United States. But here, the Virgin of Guadalupe had the Son of God beat by a long shot. She's the patron saint of Mexico, and her statutes appear in every nook and cranny in the city. A few days ago, when walking the Roma neighborhood, I spotted a statue of a Virgin nestled in a knot-hole of a tree trunk. I had no idea why she was so popular or what miracles she had done.

He glanced up again. "Her feast is coming up next week.

You can cover the story for the paper and at the same time, see the shrine. It'll be worth it."

"Hmm . . . but what about the crowds? Ten million visitors a year?"

"Aren't you used to crowds? I mean we have to be, in this profession." When I didn't respond, he added, "The Virgin heals if you pray to her."

I stopped typing for a moment. Why on earth would he think I needed healing of any kind? Do I act like an emotional basket case? My hope was to get over Marcelo without replacing him with another man. But Enrique didn't need to know that.

"I'm telling you, you should visit her shrine," Enrique repeated.

"I know. I will—someday."

"You should."

"My neighbor said the same thing the other day," I told Enrique. "She was telling me about her alcoholic husband. How he had tried Alcoholics Anonymous and failed in the twelve-step program. But with a single visit to the Virgin, he never hit the bottle again. "La Virgencita," she says, "performs miracles."

Enrique listened carefully to my story. "See? I'll bet she'd go with you. I mean, if you didn't want to go alone."

"No, that's all right. If I'm going to go, I want to go alone."

Okay, so he's not referring to my particular emotional basket case personality, he was offering a friendly tourist suggestion, that's all. I hadn't thought about the cultural aspect. He had a point. It was a basic cultural thing to do. "Thanks for the advice, Enrique, I'll think about it."

That afternoon, with the idea of a visit to the Virgin still fresh in my mind, I talked to Guido about covering Virgin's feast day for the paper, and he gave me the go-ahead.

Maybe making a pilgrimage to the Virgin of Guadalupe for personal reasons wasn't such a bad idea, either. Maybe it would help me unload the burden I was carrying around, the weight of the past and the unhealthy relationship with Marcelo. Yes, I was glad I was doing this.

Since I had a week to prepare for my visit to the shrine, I thought I should at least practice praying to the Virgin and offer her something more spontaneous than my conventional "Hail Mary" prayer. If not, she might not recognize me and all my lame prayers about Marcelo would be sent straight to her celestial spam folder.

The problem was I was used to praying to God the Father. The image of a wise old man stuck in my brain. When I prayed to Him, I could always hear God the Father's voice speaking to me. It was that deep voice that sounded regal, like James Earl Jones telling me what to do.

I also prayed to Jesus, who was a thirty-year-old miracle worker in my mind. But praying to Mary, well, that was a strange and hard thing to do. I hadn't updated my Catholic image of Mary coddling Baby Jesus so praying to her felt like I was praying to a young girl who was in high school. Something was wrong with me.

Was it just me, or were a lot of would-be *guadalupanos* out there who would like to pray to the Virgin but were discriminating against Her because she appeared too young? I had to get over my age bias against the Mother of God. It was unsettling. I asked for guidance and after the third attempt, I managed to pray to the Mother of God. I got past my stock *Hail Mary* prayer, and asked for help with trusting people again.

Wouldn't you know it, who else got drift of my going to the shrine but Malena was ready to teach me about the Virgin of Guadalupe the following day? Of course, she *heard* that I was going to cover the feast day. She already was carrying around a book for me to read. First, she asked if she could come with me to the shrine but I told her no.

"You sure?" Malena asked.

"Positive."

"Well, I'm here to rescue you. I brought you this book. A classic."

I took the book and glanced at the title, *The Wonder of Guadalupe*."

"It'll help you learn all about the shrine and the miracles associated with the Virgin."

"Thanks, Malena."

"It talks all about how the Virgin appeared to the Aztec Indian Juan Diego, and how she asked him to gather roses in the winter when roses don't normally grow. But the roses appeared on Tepeyac Hill. That's one of the miracles."

"Are you going to tell me the whole story now or are you going to let me read it?"

"I'm just telling you *some* of it. So Juan Diego gathered all the roses in his cloak and when he went to open his cloak to show the bishop, the image of the Virgin of Guadalupe was imprinted on his cloak."

"So that's the cloak that I'll see at the shrine?"

"The very one. Now that's the last thing I'm saying. That's all the proof the Bishop needed. He built a church on the spot where she had appeared, just as Virgin had asked."

"The same spot where the Basilica is today?"

"Yes. Well, right next to it. The chapel on Tepeyac Hill. You have to read the book. That's all I'm going to say about it."

I really saw no reason to read the book with Ms. Spark Notes at my side.

"That's it?" I asked Malena.

"I just told you that's all I'm going to say about it."

"Even though you told me everything already, I'm still reading the book."

"I didn't tell you everything, *chica*. Believe me, there's a lot more."

She was right. Malena was always right. It just killed me. I took a tiny peek at the book when I got home. Next thing I knew, the evening was gone and I was on page 147. Besides what Malena had already told me, I learned the miracles associated with the Virgin didn't stop with her imprint on the cloak of Juan Diego. That very cactus-fiber cloak was called *the tilma*. It was supposed to last 20 years before disintegrating, but *the tilma* has lasted almost 500 years. Scientists have been unable to explain it. Sophisticated modern tests have proved the image is not made up of any kind of paint or any modern pigment.

I snapped *The Wonder of Guadalupe* shut. *Wow.* By the time I finished the book, I was convinced that The Virgin of Guadalupe was in the Major Leagues of Miracle Making. Up there with God the Father and the parting of the sea, with Jesus multiplying loaves of bread and raising Lazarus from the dead.

I began looking forward to Monday. I would tell the Virgin of Guadalupe the whole long and twisted story of Marcelo and ask for her healing so I could move forward on mending my heart. To put all the pieces back together again, pretty please. Like Humpty Dumpty. That would be a major miracle in heart repair.

Monday came, and I took the Metro to the northern suburb of Tepeyac, where the Basilica of the Virgin of Guadalupe was located. Coming out of the Metro station, I joined a growing stream of people heading toward the Basilica. Sacred music blasted from loudspeakers set up on the street, and stores were selling religious souvenirs on the road leading to the Virgin. Flower vendors shouted, "Flowers for the Virgin, *tres mil pesos.*"

As I approached the Basilica, it struck me that the Shrine of the Virgin of Guadalupe wasn't made up of one church but two. I saw an old Basilica, a chapel on Tepeyac Hill, which I remembered reading about. John and Jacqueline Kennedy had visited the old Basilica when he was president. The new Basilica reminded me of a sports stadium since it was a round architectural wonder built with many entrances.

A man on his knees on the plaza inched toward the Basilica entrance with his wife holding his hand. I shamelessly stared. Wow, that religious fervor was just like the people in the slides I'd seen in my high school Spanish class.

Standing at one of the Basilica's entrances, I spotted the framed portrait of the Virgin hanging above the altar, but it was too far to see well from the doorway. I inhaled deeply. I was dying to see her up close but a Mass was being held. I eyed the sides of the Basilica where people were disappearing into confessional booths. Oh, no, that's not where I want to go.

A guide was explaining the history of the Basilica to her tour group next to me. My ears perked up. "In order to see the Virgin's image up close, we go behind the altar. A passageway leads to a lower level. We can view the Virgin from the lower floor so it doesn't distract from the Mass on the ground floor. We'll head over there in a little bit."

So that's how it worked.

I sprang to action. Sprinted past the people spilling their sins in the confessional booths, past the tour group, past the priest, and past the kneeling crowds to stand in line to see the image of the Virgin. Along with half the population of Mexico. Where were all these people coming from? Oh my Gosh, it was a Monday.

I stood in the line for about twenty minutes before I tapped the shoulder of the woman standing in front of me. "You here to see the Virgin?"

"Sí, señora, we're all waiting for our turn."

"Oh, just checking," I said with a sense of relief. "For a moment there, I thought I was accidentally in a confessional line."

I didn't pretend to be saint-like or anything, but with all that time in the line, I began really praying in a spontaneous way that the *Virgencita* would help me with healing.

Since I didn't know what to do once I reached the image of the Virgin, I took the "monkey see, monkey do" approach. As people in front of me in the line drew closer to the framed image of the Virgin, they stepped on a moving sidewalk, made the sign of the cross and began praying. I could see the woman in front of me dabbing her eyes at the sight of the framed image of the Virgin imprinted on the cloak made of cloth from agave fiber.

I was next. I stepped on the moving sidewalk and got a first-hand look at the beloved Mexican icon that had fascinated me since high school. Way, way up there. There she was, the Virgin of Guadalupe. The cloak with the Virgin image glistened in a gold frame. I gazed at her from way, way down on the moving sidewalk. Her faded blue-green cloak was covered with stars and a robe. This was the cloak that no science could explain.

Her hands were folded in prayer. Her eyes were downcast, as if she were looking directly at me, the pilgrim.

"Holy Mary, Mother of God, I'm finally here." I crossed myself. My lips moved feverishly, my palms folded and the standard "Hail Mary" tumbled out first. Next, as I was giving her an earful on evil Marcelo and about to ask her for some serious healing, the moving sidewalk swept me to the other side to make room for the throngs of people behind me.

I stepped off. Geez, I barely said hello and never had the chance to say goodbye to the Virgin. I only really got a glimpse. *Seconds*. Would my prayer even count? I hadn't experienced a Virgin epiphany. Hadn't been touched by *The Light*. My eyes were the same hazel as they had always been. Wait, Sara. Did you really expect a miraculous healing of the heart from seeing the Virgin up close in her shrine? In the corner of my heart, the part still in pieces, said yes. But in my head, I was telling myself that healing wouldn't come in an instant, like a bolt of lightning. Emotional healing takes time.

I left the shrine, walking past the street peddlers hawking Virgin souvenirs: past tiny Virgin figurines, past Virgin glow-in-the-dark bumper stickers, past Virgin rosaries, and Virgin medals.

I should buy a Virgin statue or necklace or something, I thought, as a remembrance, or as a kind of good-luck charm like many Mexicans do. It couldn't hurt. I approached a vendor hunched over under the weight of dozens of silver crosses and rosaries hanging around his neck. He stretched out an arm to showcase dozens of Virgin medals and sepulchers for sale. "Two for twenty pesos," he said.

"Do you happen to have a keychain with the Virgin on a skateboard?" I asked him. I thought it would be the perfect souvenir to reflect my experience on the moving sidewalk.

He shook his head. He must have been used to weird requests from tourists because all he said was, "No, señorita. *Lo siento*. Sorry."

"Never mind." I bought a silver Virgin medal instead. One that I could wear around my neck under my clothes. I pulled it over my neck right away. I didn't need a Virgin statue for my apartment, that was for sure. My living room already had a Virgin painting on the wall. Actually, the painting was of a Virgin with seven daggers piercing her heart. It took suffering to a whole new level. When I mentioned the violent image to Malena, she had told me there were Virgins of all different sorts, and the one hanging on my wall was probably the Virgin of Sorrows.

Later that evening, after I had filed the story for the paper, I got to thinking that all the Virgin of Guadalupe images made more sense after my visit. I could understand why I see so many Mexicans wearing amulets around their necks and plastering their dashboards with stickers of the Virgin's image. A medal or a sticker is a good way to remember her image after getting only a fleeting glimpse of her on the moving sidewalk. I bet the souvenir vendors could make even more money selling T-shirts that say I GOT A GLIMPSE OF THE VIRGIN.

8

Why Can't I Be 29 Forever?

E very birthday is perfect in my eyes if it has the three essential things; a cake the size of a Mazda, candles melting into a messy wax, and someone singing "Happy Birthday" off-key. But this birthday was different. I was turning thirty. And thirty sounded, well, like an expiration date on the bottom of a milk carton.

Well, it at least looked and felt like I was losing my *vim* and *voom*, let alone my *vavoom*. I could count the lines around my eyes and hair sprouted in new places on my upper lip and poked out of my chin—what better proof I was fast losing my *vim* and *voom*, let alone my *vavoom*?

Technically, I had one more week of being twenty-nine when Alex called me to wish me a Happy Big Three-Oh.

"My birthday isn't until next week, Alex."

"Oh, I know. I couldn't wait to tell you all the news."

"What news?"

"Carla's getting engaged."

"To who?"

"You are not going to believe it. Ready? Some guy she met in an elevator."

"I'm not surprised. An elevator is the singles bar for New York's workaholics. Anyway, I think marriage is worse than death."

"You're just hurt. That's why you think that way. Hold on. You ready for another piece of gossip?"

"No. Give me a hint." Oh, but I was. All of a sudden, it struck me that I hadn't heard gossip in months. I was so busy gnawing at the facts, sucking the juice out of scrawny bones of events. Facts were coming out of my ears. Gossip? It was like being fed a feast after fasting on a Good Friday.

"Ashley is getting married," Alex announced.

"Ashley?" I exhaled. "Oh, I knew that. Not know, know, but expected that. Where have you been? She and Greg have been together forever."

"Well, they have a date set for the wedding. June something. You're invited. They called me because they couldn't reach you. By the way, you told no one about running off to Mexico."

"I know."

"And did you know, Miss Smarty Pants, that Nicole is getting divorced?"

"Nah, you're kidding. She's only been married a year. Got any juicy details?"

"Nope. Nobody's talking. Just that she has a new boyfriend."

Gee, thanks for reminding me about that last one, Alex. People work fast in New York when they are sliding into thirty. Chances of snatching a male specimen any time soon was next to nil. I wasn't even getting a distant date.

"So—what about you?" Alex asked right before hanging up.

See? I knew he was going to ask that. "Have you buried the ghost of Marcelo down there?" Alex continued.

"Well, to give you an idea, in order to keep track of them, I had to get an Excel spread sheet. I am attracting guys from as far away as Malaysia."

"What? Like how many?" Alex asked.

"I'm not telling."

"C'mon cuz, fess up."

"Okay, zero."

"Did you say zero?

"Still romantically impaired."

Alex groaned. "You mean two thousand miles away, with a fresh start, a new job, and you still aren't giving anyone a chance?"

"It's not really my fault, really, Alex. I just feel I must protect myself just a bit."

"Just a bit?" Alex asked. You're still hurting, Sara, and got your defenses up."

"Okay, maybe a little more than a bit. You may be right. These days, I'm French-kissing my doormat when I get home."

"You have a scratch on your soul, Sara, that's all."

"That's not it, Alex, but do you know that's what the spines of a cactus are for?

"No, I don't *want to know* what the spines of a cactus are for. You're changing the subject. But I do know my beautiful cousin is not enjoying herself down in Mexico."

"Well, the spines protect the plant from predators. Just like me, I'm wearing invisible spines on my all over me so that if men try to get close, I poke them away."

"You have to give somebody a chance."

"I know."

"You *know* but your heart isn't convinced."

"You should see what they do down here, Alex."

"What do you mean?"

"Middle-aged couples make out in public all the time. Not just teenagers. You wouldn't believe it. They clinch. It's revolting."

"No kidding."

"Yeah. Royal slobber. Right on the subway platform. And guess what? I have to watch their slurpy, sloppy kissing It's like reading a mushy Hallmark card every day."

"Well, I think it's great. Why hide love if you have it?"

"No, no. You don't understand. It's *disgusting*. You know what I want to do? I want to blow up a paper bag and sneak up, and catch them in their kissy-kissies and smash it above their heads. *Bang!* Wouldn't it be wonderful?"

"No, it sounds kind of mean, like you're still hurt. Sara, they probably don't have much privacy at home. They might live with their families or something. So they catch up on their affection in public."

"Well, it's not fair. How come they can enjoy kissing so much? Meanwhile, I am turning thirty and kissless?"

"Listen, Sara, being lonely is still better than a screwed-up relationship like the one you had with Marcelo. So you're not ready for another relationship yet? No wonder. Hanging on to that bastard so long has made you cynical."

"Maybe you're right. But I do know there are married guys lurking, Alex. Married and looking to prey on naïve, single, and trusting women like me."

"Yeah, but this time, you're on the lookout for them."

Alex's phone call got me thinking. I realized how jaded I was, and more worried about avoiding a Mr. Wrong than finding a Mr. Right. The truth of the matter was my social life could have been better, too. If I just let someone, besides Francisco, get to know me. Even at the office, I was lacking in the friend department except for Malena. The rest of my female co-workers, namely, Emma and Kate, still made me feel shrimp-like because of their crispy British accents and vocabulary digested from the *Oxford* dictionary.

I was funless and after months of living here, still friendless.

So when Emma announced in the newsroom that a group of *Observer* reporters were meeting informally at a cantina nearby for drinks, my ears perked up. Anybody who wanted to go should meet at 6 p.m. Well, I saw this invitation as a small window of opportunity to get to know everyone better at work, even though I wasn't one to mingle. Especially since Enrique and Malena said they couldn't make it. With my rookie reputation to live down, I mean, I was surprised that Emma didn't *disinvite* me. This may be my only chance to chum around with my colleagues. I decided to go and see what developed.

Only five of us showed up at the cantina: the British girls Emma and Kate, Texan Dave, Ashok and me. Emma ordered a round of beers, surveyed the group of us at the table and asked in her crispiest voice, "Did any of you lovelies see the article in yesterday's newspaper on careers?"

Of course, Kate was the first. "The one that ranked over 400 occupations in the U.S.? I saw it. It was in *The New York Times*, but I didn't read it."

"Well, I did. Guess which job ranked the worst?"

"A coal miner?" Dave asked.

"A newspaper reporter," Emma said.

"Hmph!" Kate shrugged. "Well, at least we aren't crammed into a cubicle crunching numbers for a spread sheet. That would be worse."

The beers came. We toasted to the "World's Worst Job." We sipped ice cold *Victorias*.

"Personally," Dave said, "I think it makes us stand out in the crowd. Beats the software engineers and accountants."

"Right." Ashok said. "The world's worst job. What does that make us? The world's worst workers?"

Emma pointed to the one last glass of beer untouched. "I ordered an extra one. I was going to drink this, but have decided not to. I'm going to give the last glass of beer as a prize to whoever convinces me a news reporter is the most awful job."

"I'm in." Kate said.

"Me, too," Dave said.

"Sounds fun," Ashok said.

I didn't say anything. Majority rules, anyway.

That's when Kate said, "Ashok, you go first."

"Me? Okay. I'm happy to hear we're number one in something. Unfortunately, we're treated like number two in everything else."

"We're ranked last," I corrected, "I mean, that's what she said, according to *The New York Times*."

"Right," Ashok went on. "Well, that makes us number 400 of 400 occupations. Which goes to show you. A newspaper reporter is the world's worst job because we lack respect."

Dave eyed Ashok, and said, "You got a point but it isn't

terribly convincing."

Emma nodded, and turned to her friend. "Kate?"

"It is fearsomely hard to imagine how this profession of a news reporter has mutated into one akin to a doctor working 24/7 in a hospital emergency room. We are on call. Things happen for no discernible reason and at all hours of the night. We news reporters are expected to drop everything and record the turn of events. It's rubbish. We cannot relax."

"Point well taken," Emma said. "Reflective of the awfulness, but not persuasive enough." She scanned the group. "Agreed?"

"Agreed!" We said in unison.

Kate turned to Dave. "Well, Dave?"

"Shitty pay. Twelve-hour days suck. Deadlines that make your ass itch."

We all laughed.

"That was a good one, Dave," Ashok said.

"Should we give him the beer?" Emma asked.

"Yes!" Kate said. "He deserves it."

I nodded.

Dave reached for the bottle of beer.

Emma raised her hand. "Wait a minute. We haven't heard from Sara."

"Me?"

"Yes, you."

"Oh, let's see." I looked down and stretched my fingers on the table to study my bitten-off fingernails and tried to think of something clever to say. When I needed witty words the most, I couldn't think of one. What came to mind was the Mexican-American War incident that drove my fellow reporters to treat me differently. So I said, "News reporters make mistakes. What's awful about this job is that a mistake has a very long life-span." I lifted my eyes.

Heads nodded.

I saw Emma exchange glances with Kate before she asked, "That's all?"

Since I had shrunken and was being ingested by the British

girls, I added, "No. I mean to say . . . um . . . that I'm a news reporter because I'm terrible at everything else."

They all laughed.

"Me, too," Dave added.

"Well . . ." Emma said. "Quite amusing."

"So I get the beer?" I asked.

"Did she earn it?" Emma asked the group.

"Yeah, just let her have the beer," Dave said.

"I think she *earned* it," Ashok said.

I turned to Emma, "What about you? You haven't said anything yet." I was itching to hear her story.

"Yeah, Emma," Dave said.

"Well, to be frank with all of you, extinction is the operative word for a news reporter. With declining subscriptions and dwindling advertising, news reporting is going the way of the Siberian tiger, the California Condor and the Giant Panda."

"Ahem . . ." Ashok said.

Silence. More silence broken up by some clearing of throats, as if my colleagues were suddenly gargling with mouthwash.

Dave grinned at Emma. "That was certainly well said."

"I think you deserve the beer, Emma," Kate said.

I almost spit up with jealousy. How could Emma sound so eloquent? California condor and Giant Panda? "Braggart," I muttered under my breath, making sure it was low enough so nobody could hear. I was still grinding my teeth over Emma's "quite amusing" remark but I'd show her. I cleared my throat too before I deadlocked eyes with her and said, "Eloquent, Emma, but not quite convincing."

I felt a gust of wind and it was Emma's eyes blinking.

"Hey, everyone," Ashok said to diffuse the mood, which had a whiff of a catfight. "How about another turn? Before Dave or Sara start fighting over the one *Victoria* beer? Now I have a much better idea of what I'm up against in this gladiatorial game, so I'd like to have another chance."

"That's called cheating," Dave said.

"Well, you must prove it," Emma said. She pushed the beer forward to the center of the table. "This is an ice-cold *Victoria*, and we're all fighting for it. Should we permit him another turn?"

All nods.

"Have another go."

"Okay," Ashok's voice was full of earnest. "What is it that we mostly do? Cover deplorable politicians. Correct?"

"Yeah," I said. "Well, not me, but yeah, news reporters in general, I guess."

Dave nodded.

Kate just listened.

"Go on," Emma said.

"They're absolutely filthy," Ashok continued. "Corrupt. Greedy. Like rodents. But we must track them anyway and write about their droppings. What does this make us? The ultimate pest control."

We all laughed.

Ashok won the beer.

We continued soaking up the atmosphere of the cantina. I studied the strange mannequins of costumed bullfighters encased in window display cabinets. On the walls hung oil paintings of bullfighting scenes. All of a sudden, I started sneezing uncontrollably.

Achoo!

"Bless you," Dave said. "It's the dust. Man, this place is old."

Achoo!

Dave pointed to the windows. "I can't even see out the windows."

Achoo!

"Don't you think it has so much character?" Emma said.

Achoo!

"I bet the bathrooms are disgusting," Kate added. "But they do have a *rockola* or jukebox, which lends itself to some character."

Ashok pointed to an encased statue of the Virgin that was framed with flowers. "Look over there. An altar of the Virgin of Guadalupe."

"You're right," I said, and gazed at the multi-colored bulbs flashing around the frame.

The waiter came to take our order and we decided on shrimp soup. Waiting for our food to arrive, I ventured into the world of gossip. "So . . .," I said aloud, trying to think of something personal I wanted to find out about my colleagues. "How long has everyone been in Mexico?" We compared notes. Emma, two years, Kate, a year and half, Dave a year. I was surprised to learn that most of my co-workers said they were planning to stay for a long time but they weren't sure how long. Ashok turned to include me, "How about you? How long are you staying?"

Were his black laser eyes twinkling or was I imagining it? "Um, a year. How about you?"

"Haven't decided."

As I sat there nibbling on some peanuts, I regarded my fellow reporters in a new light. They were not strangers anymore. They were my colleagues. We were a Newshood. The Newshood of the World's Worst Job. The Newshood of Pest Control. And, what do homies do? Offer *chismes*. Gossip, right? Shouldn't we be sharing more *chismes*? Shouldn't we be swapping stories from the Newshood? Sharing our sources in case any of us gets sick?

So far, no gossip. Just facts. None before dinner came. During the course of the evening, I was periodically struck mute by hearing BBC English snippets coming from Kate, listening to how "daft," a person is, how "brilliant" an idea is or how everything turned into "rubbish," that a cloud of inferiority settled on me again. To make matters worse, I found out Emma and Kate had a bank account with supplemental income coming in from Britain every month. Monthly remittances. I didn't ask why because money was considered a taboo topic, but I felt a little jealous. They weren't worried about paying rent and so they could freelance and do music and art features for a variety of Mexican newspapers or magazines. It all made sense. Besides all this, I was only a one beer or one glass of wine kind of lady. The others drained freshwater lakes. The only common ground that I felt was that we spoke English.

After eating, we sat around looking at each other like what the heck are we going to talk about now? Texan Dave ventured out of his reporter mode and said, "Can you believe that we are all down here, working for pesos, when Mexicans go to our countries looking for work? How weird is that?"

"It's genuinely bizarre," Emma said. She was sipping a cocktail and suddenly lifted her glass. "To ex-pats. Indians, British," and she looked at Dave, then winked at me, "Americans."

It felt great to be included and I clinked my water to their beers. "Wait," I said, "there is a big difference."

Eyes swiveled to land on me and everybody lowered their glasses. "What do you mean?" Emma asked.

"We choose to be here. Mexicans leave their families and risk their lives to cross because they want a better life." I was surprised that I had found more than a few words to say in the commanding presence of the British women.

"Oh, Sara, that's way too heavy for tonight," Dave said.

"Think about it," I went on. "All we need is a visa stamp at the airport for six months and we can live here freely. We don't have to stay in hiding, working in a shadow economy, like they do in the U.S.," I said with a fluency that surprised even me.

Emma turned her gaze at me. "Lovely how Sara has added a splash of seriousness to the evening's banter, isn't it?" Emma said.

"Right," Kate added. "I believe you're requiring us to reassess our priorities and ponder our place in the world."

"Well, that's what I think," I said, and left it at that. After a timid *clink clink,* followed by a subtle *¡Salud!* a toast that I had dampened, I slumped into my chair and fell quiet, thinking. See? I knew I didn't fit in. Should I go back to snowy New York? For the first time since I came to Mexico, I longed to be in New York with my cousin Alex and eat some Chinese take-out, especially Jimmy Chang's fried rice. At this point, with my mood so gloomy, I would have even settled for bowling or playing poker with my parents and sisters in Michigan. While others drank happily, I tore my napkin into shreds under the table.

Ashok turned to me and said in a whisper. "I think you had a good point. Don't let them make you feel bad."

"Thanks," I mumbled. He looked into my eyes a little longer than normal. Wow, those penetrating eyes could burn a hole through my temples. Was there something there beyond helping me to save face? He would look at me and I would look at him, and I would look away, embarrassed.

The next day, I went back to throwing myself a pity party as my thirtieth birthday crept a day closer. I tried to look at the bright side. I had ventured into living in a foreign country. It was a tiny part of another world but I guess it would qualify enough to be able to check off "see the world" on my bucket list before I turn 30. Even if friends weren't swarming at my door, I had survived a reputation-ruining incident. I was on my way to a new career.

That didn't cheer me up for long. That gnawing feeling kept coming back. I had no family around and only one friend that I could deeply relate to. It was probably silly. Okay, it was silly. No matter how old I was, I still yearned for a birthday cake, candles, and friends around. My birthday was one day that I didn't have to share with anybody else, not Abraham Lincoln, not Martin Luther King, not George Washington. I decided to call my older sister in Michigan to remind her that my birthday was only days away, and I still hadn't made any friends.

"Feeling old isn't the word," I began. "It's an abyss, a hell hole down here without friends."

"What about the last time we talked? You had made friends with one girl. Remember?"

"Malena?

"That was it. What about her? Is she still your friend?"

"Yeah, but she's kind of older. Way older, like Mom's age."

"So?"

"Okay, I have one. One, that's it."

"One is enough, Sara. We can't be greedy about friends, you

know. You want to move back to Detroit?"

"Oh, God, no."

"Well, turning thirty wouldn't be that big a deal over here. You might even be happy about it. I'd make you a big bowl of pasta, we'd have some cake and we'd sing to you."

"Well, I'm not in Detroit, so now what?" This was the sister who had turned thirty the year before, which naturally made my aging milestone anti-climactic.

"How about if I send you a funny card? Something like an over-the-hill gag?"

"Nah, don't bother, I'll never get it."

"Sure you will. I'll go to the drugstore today and post it tomorrow. Your birthday is still six days away."

"You don't get it. Mexican mail delivery from the U.S. is surreal. Envelopes, cards, packages all get sucked into some giant black hole."

"Okay, if more than a month goes by and you don't get my card, call me again, okay?" she went on. "What is a Mexican black hole, anyway?"

"Customs."

After I hung up with her, I thanked my lucky stars for my cousin Alex. He was my lifeline to communication with people in the States. I would package up letters to my family and friends. He would not only pay for my DHL package to get to the States, but he'd distribute the letters.

That day, and the next day, and the day after that, I wallowed. I checked the mail once, twice, okay, it might have been three times a day. Nothing.

On the day of my birthday, I looked in the mirror the first thing in the morning and told myself, Happy Birthday, Sara! You're looking younger by the minute!

And then a tiny voice inside of me squeaked at me with questions: "Are you tired, run down, listless? Do you opt out of parties? Are you unpopular? The answer to all your problems is in the little bottle of Dr. Mercola's vitamins.

I picked up the bottle of vitamins on the bathroom sink and read the back of the bottle. The little voice returned, "The answer to all your problems is in this little bottle— Dr. Mercola's Supercharged Vitamin Magic." Couldn't hurt if I popped two tablets into my mouth today, maybe it will make me extra peppy. I swallowed them with a big glass of water.

Afterwards, I went to work and looked under the dictionaries scattered around the newsroom, just in case there were birthday presents hidden under them and then double checked the newspaper wire basket where the office boys deposited staff mail. Nothing.

I would be even happier about my official day of birth if I got a letter addressed to "Press." I resigned myself to receiving not one birthday card from my family. *Of course not.* What was I thinking? That Superman, Santa Claus or the Tooth Fairy would fly a few thousand miles south and make a special delivery? Fate wanted me to celebrate my birthday alone.

I did receive an urgent message, though. A panicky-worded message from Alex. He was asking me what furniture I wanted to save out of my apartment. He informed me that I was losing my apartment because the building's manager ran into my sub-leased illegal tenant when she was asking about fixing the washing machine. He was telling me this on my birthday? How dare he. I wrote in big fat letters "SAVE ALL MY BOOKS." He wrote back, "Nobody can hang up their coats 'cause of those damn books taking up the closet at work, REMEMBER?"

Oh, yeah, that's right. Well, he didn't have to get all upset about it and tell me I was losing my apartment on my birthday. Didn't he remember that this was my actual birthday?

Deadlines are deadlines so I managed to return to tinkering with the article I was writing. The story was about Mexico's plans for installing new ground stations and getting more satellites. The topic was about as exciting as writing about a bag of mud. It was detailed and technical and progress was slow. A few other reporters were clicking away on their stories too. Photographers were going in and out. One by one, as reporters were leaving, the office got quieter and quieter. When I finally looked up, it was 10:46 p.m. and I was the only one left in the newsroom. The phone rang. Guido.

"Sara, can I see you a minute? It's about a story you filed," he said in an urgent voice.

"Sure. Be right there." My heart raced. Great. He had used that same "I-need-to-see-you-tone" when he hauled me into his office after I wrote about the Mexican-American War. Had I written something that irritated readers like that? Nothing came to mind but I surely could have. As I made my way to Guido's office, I could almost see my boss flapping his arms and reminding me of the consequences of reporting on unfavorable government activities. Standing in front of Guido's shut door brought me back to reality. "Come in!" boomed the stern voice of my boss. Trembling, I turned the doorknob.

"SURPRISE!" Faces of all the people I really knew in Mexico smiled at me. There was Malena, Guido, there was Enrique, even the finance editor I hardly knew, and all my fellow reporters.

They stood and sang "Happy Birthday to you . . ."

I held back the tears.

They continued to sing *"Las Mañanitas,"* a Mexican birthday song. And that's when I began to cry. "Wow, I didn't suspect anything. How did you manage to hide it?"

"We truly surprised you, did we?" asked Kate.

I nodded.

"Brilliant!" Emma replied. "Shall we thank Guido and Enrique? They organized it. With Malena's help."

I grinned at Guido, Enrique, and Malena and showered them with thank-you's.

"Here, have a drink," said Dave the Texan, handing me a beer, "I've been waiting too long to get started on the appetizers."

I curled my fingers around a beer. That's when I noticed the carefully prepared *botanas*: slices of cucumber, avocado, and all kinds of nuts. Best of all, there was a huge vanilla birthday cake with thirty candles on it and "Sara" written across the top.

"Open your presents!" Malena shouted.

Presents? I had received presents?

"Yeah, open them!" Ashok roared and again his eyes lingered on mine a little longer than normal. Should I read something into that lingering look? Was meta messaging going on?

My presents were not gag ones, not the "you're over the hill" kind, but nice ones: an illustration of Mexico City, a sweater, and a few handicrafts. Ashok had given me a book, a biography on the Mexican artist Frida Kahlo.

9

A Romantic Rumble

Ashok's penetrating eyes had been beaming melting messages, after all. He asked me out the day after my surprise birthday party. This would be my first date in Mexico. I know, I know, I had written off all men. But Ashok was a colleague, and I thought, what the heck, I'll keep it easy breezy and not think about building a relationship with him. Mulling over my goal to get over Marcelo, I realized that maybe I'd been too serious before. Maybe my co-workers were right. I probably needed to lighten up. Of course, I would not lighten up enough to forget that I wasn't ready for any relationship that would be long-lasting. So why not leave it to chance for once. If nothing happened, I could have some fun in the meantime and live for today, like half the world does.

So I spent many evenings with Ashok. We didn't do all that much. I wouldn't call it a romance, exactly. It was more of a hanging out together. We often listened to music or explored bookshops together.

We hit a bit of a snag one evening when Ashok invited me to his place for a home-cooked meal for the following Saturday night. When I said yes, Ashok told me he wasn't going to cook the whole meal for me, just the vegetarian main course. He asked what I would contribute in terms of homemade cooking.

"Um . . . I eat *comida corridas* every day. Those cheap lunch specials at the restaurants are my saviors."

"In other words, you don't cook."

"Right."

"Do you know how to cook?"

"Well, let's just say, my usual dinner is bread and cheese or beans and rice."

"How about making a fruit salad or something?

"That, I think, I can do."

"Perfect."

I mean, after all, what could go wrong with making a fruit salad? Time consuming but definitely doable. I thought Ashok's eyes would pop out when I made sure about the dish. "All I need to do is buy a bunch of fresh fruit and cut it all up, isn't that it?"

"That's it." He shook his head in disbelief. "Do you think you can do that?"

At that moment, it was really obvious how the *comida corridas* had a corruptive influence on me." Relying on eating out in restaurants had ruined the chance of improving my cooking skills. I mean, for three and a half dollars, the lunch special was huge. I silently ticked off, I get tortillas, beans, soup, a meat and a dessert. What's more, I could never ever go back to Taco Bell in the U.S.

Making a fruit salad did mean I had to go to an outdoor market, which would take me one or two steps closer to actually cooking. But this home cooking event was five days away.

* * *

Saturday morning, I grabbed my never-used-before mesh bag and off I went to one of those open-air street markets called a *tianguis*, which mostly sold fruit and vegetables.

Uh oh. The stalls in the open market bulged with UFOs: unidentifiable food objects. The first stall I came upon displayed large hairy and tuby things. Dozens of these large hairy and tuby things stacked one on top of the other to form pyramids. I picked up one of the light tan objects. It was as heavy as a rock. "*¿Qué es ésto?*" I asked what it was.

"*Jícama,*" the señora said from behind the stand.

I tapped the object against the edge of the stall a couple of times. Tap, tap. Pause. Hard as stone. "*¿Puedo comerlo?*" Can I eat it?

"How many will you take, señorita?"

"Ah . . . no, *gracias.*" I shot her a quick grin and weaved my way through the crowd. I didn't have the heart to tell her I was afraid of breaking my tooth if I bit into one of her moon rocks. After all, I barely had enough money for food and rent, let alone for any emergency dental visit.

I stopped in front of another mystery mound. These objects were perfectly round in shades of yellow and blotchy lime green. Were they oversized lemons? Strange enormous limes? I asked the man hovering over them.

"*Naranjas,*" he said.

Oranges? Really? The citrus balls I was familiar with in the U.S. were brighter than highway cones.

"How many kilos do you want?" the vendor asked.

I shook my palm in a polite no thank you.

"Take them, good price," he snapped.

"All right, five kilos."

"Five kilos, señorita?"

"Five kilos, *sí.*" I had no idea how many oranges I was actually buying since I never understood kilos, but I felt guilty squeezing them without buying any. Five sounded like the most perfect number.

Wait a minute. Five kilos does not mean a couple of pounds. Five kilos does mean I got a back-breaking sack of oranges. Dragging my five kilos past the papaya stands, past the cucumber stands, past the tomato stand, I took a breather in front of an herbal medicine stall.

I peered at the dried herbs in burlap bags with a sign stuck in each bag announcing which ailment it cured. I ran my fingers through odd-shaped twigs, flower bits and dried leaves that promised cures for Varicose Veins, Ovary Pains, Persistent Cough, Memory Lapse, and Fright. A sack that had dried rose petals with the sign promised "Lover's Cure." I lifted a few of the dried petals and ran them through my fingers.

"What can I give you?" A señora appeared from behind her stall. I told her that I was just looking. She waved her arms dramatically over her magical bundles. "Cures for everything, señorita."

I asked the medicine woman how rose petals could possibly cure love problems.

"Burning the petals removes enemy's curse," she said, thrusting a handful of rose petals to my nostrils. "Mixed with oil, I make you love potion, too." She winked.

"Another time." That was the last thing I needed in my life. I turned and scolded myself. I had come for fruit to make a salad and was investigating rose petals for romance.

* * *

Success!

That night, I successfully heaved my mesh bag onto the counter top, all five kilos of oranges. Ashok caught a few of the orangey yellowy balls before they rolled off the counter, but all he said was: "You chop the potatoes and I'll start the curry."

"Okay, do you realize these splotchy yellow lime balls are oranges?"

"Yes, I do."

"Five kilos worth. Do you have any idea how much five kilos is?"

"11.369 pounds."

"Oh." He didn't have to be so smart-alecky and nerdy about it.

"Where's your juicer to squeeze all these?"

"In the cupboard."

"Are you ready to sip some fresh orange juice with your

curry dish?"

Silence.

I reached for the hand juicer, squeezed an orange, one trickle after another to barely fill a cup and held it up to show him. "This, by the way, is instead of the fruit salad."

"Interesting combination, I must say."

I refrained from being sarcastic and simply said, "It'll be refreshing." Never mind that I had practically slipped a disc dragging oranges across the city, down the Metro steps, up the Metro steps, through the streets and all the way to his house. We would definitely have a pitcher of freshly squeezed orange juice to go with our curry. Too bad if you were dreaming of the fruit salad, Master Chefo. I buckled down to cut up the potatoes.

Ashok made his curry, standing enthralled by his pot on the stove. He began to hum something that sounded like a Bollywood song. It was catchy, full of life. He tossed some yellow mustard seeds into the hot oil. When they sizzled, he shook the pot until the seeds popped and added cumin, ginger and onions.

"Smells heavenly," I said.

"Last but not least, jalapeños." Pieces of chile pepper disappeared into the pot. "Did you know chili peppers were brought to India by the Portuguese?" He stirred and sniffed and hummed. "That's how jalapeños wound up in Indian curries."

"No, I didn't. But that's something like Marco Polo bringing pasta to Italy from China. Did you know that?"

He shook his head. "But am not surprised. International trade and finance in the old days."

He was competitive, that I knew. I found that intellectual edginess kind of sexy. I gazed at Ashok. His beautiful brown nose was hovering over the sizzling pot and he looked so happy humming.

"You're turning me on, cooking like that."

He stopped his hum and grinned. "It's the chiles. They give off intoxicating vapors."

"Nah, it's you."

We kissed. Tender fat lips smashed against mine. Those inky eyes that bore a hole in anyone who dared to look at him too long scared everybody off, but not me. They attracted me. We did more kissing than cooking. That was how he burned his curry sauce and I made one measly glass of orange juice rather than a whole pitcher.

"Take off your shoes," Ashok said, "let me feel your feet."

My shoes? So I was already on the excitement trail so kicked off my shoes. "Geez, I hope my feet don't stink...."

Ashok got up to get some coconut oil and began massaging my feet with it.

"Oh, yeah," I groaned. "That feels so good. Wow, you really know how to do a massage, don't you?"

Then he began sucking my toes.

That's when my eyeballs went to the back of my head. "Oh my, God, that feels so good!' I moaned some more and then the lights went out in the brain again.

After we made love, we sat cross-legged sitting on the floor while Ashok taught me about the stock market. He listened to me with those penetrating eyes as I made comparisons between the culture in the U.S. and Mexico. I found him intellectually stimulating and he told me I was one of the smartest people he knew. I laughed at that one. While sitar music flooded his apartment, he asked me how I felt toward him.

"It's as if . . . hmm . . . I'm falling in like." I said. "What about you?"

"Same here. You know, I'm glad it's nothing serious because I'm planning to marry a Brahmin girl from India, a wife that my family will pick out," he explained as he switched the sitar music to a Bollywood song. "It's the way we do it there." He said it as if he was saying something ordinary. Like he was changing his bed sheets or taking out the trash.

"That's nice . . . traditional and everything." At that point was I glad I hadn't revealed I was trying to forget an old boyfriend who turned out to be someone's husband, definitely something he never needed to know.

I was confused. Was he telling me this because it was the start of something or the end of something? Besides his intellect and inky eyes, I was drawn to his silky, smooth skin. He took off his shirt and let me run my fingers up his back, just to feel the silkiness. "Your skin is butter."

"Come here," he said, and pulled me close to him. He smelled of ginger and onion. I closed my eyes and he kissed my eyelids.

"Wow." My eyes slowly opened.

"What?" He traced his fingers around my mouth tenderly.

"Nothing. It's just . . . Your kisses feel good."

"Oh. You know you've got the most beautiful smile I've ever seen."

"You're just saying that." I was enjoying the feeling of being wanted. I realized that my thoughts were about to register a severe blackout caused by lack of oxygen to the brain.

We made love that night, and many nights afterwards. Weeks went by, simple and sensual weeks. Before our relationship could evolve into the next emotional level, Ashok left *The Observer* and moved on to another job.

Oddly enough, we didn't see each other after he left the paper. It struck me as a solid bit of evidence that our relationship was nothing but mutual need for companionship rather than anything even remotely resembling love. Of course, Ashok was working long hours at his new job at an international wire service, but neither one of us asked the other to even go out for a cup of coffee. We called each other now and then, but our phone calls were kept friendly and polite and centered on work. A month after getting his new job, the calls had become less frequent until they petered out altogether.

10

Love Thy Neighbor

A t the humongous black iron gates, I stood, trembling.
The American Embassy was big. Monster big. Even
from a "Be-All-That-You-Can-Be" perspective, it was still
intimidating. This concrete compound was so enormous that
it must have had its own zip code and ozone layer. The
wrought iron stakes surrounded the embassy like a moat.
Guards circled the complex—the kind of guards you didn't
want to ask any questions. Outside a line of people waiting to
get in stretched down Reforma Boulevard and probably
reached halfway to Panama. I couldn't help but wonder if this
embassy was purposely built to promote international tension.
Love Thy Neighbor? Forget about it.

I know how I would feel if I were Mexican, and my next-
door neighbor was guarding his property in the middle of *my
capital city* with an iron gate full of pointy pickets? He would be
preventing me from entering his iron gate to legal ask for a
tourist, business, or resident visa since his elephantine picket
fence appeared extremely difficult to climb, even with a ladder.

When I told Guido that I was attending a meeting on water
rights at the embassy, he had warned me of the tough security

measures. But I wasn't expecting this size of hostility. And rushing around the house to get there on time, I had forgotten the letter I was supposed to bring to show embassy officials my security clearance.

I poked my nose through the thick iron posts and in a tiny voice, no louder than the squeak of a mouse, emitted a *"Hello?"*

After several minutes, a Mexican uniformed guard strolled over from his post and began his Inquisition behind the bars of the gate:

"Show me your picture ID," the embassy security guard said.

I flashed my press badge dangling from my neck.

"The purpose of your visit?"

"A meeting. On water rights," I squeaked. "Do you want to see it more closely?" I slipped my press badge through the pointed pillars of the gate.

He barely glanced at it.

"Distinguishing scars?" he continued.

Skipping the ones over my lip and under my eye, I lifted my chin and pointed under it. "See here? Fifteen stitches. Ice skating. Want to hear how it happened?"

"No. Blood type?" the officer asked.

Honestly, the last few questions were ones that I only *thought* the guard would ask me since his *real* questions were turning into ridiculous ones. They were obviously leading to the ultimate goal of having me confess to secretly harboring a metal eyelash curler in my purse. I wanted to refuse to answer all his silly questions, but the image of a solitary confinement cell in a very remote place forced me to reply with perfunctory politeness.

A very tense twenty-five minutes went by. I was spelling my last name "Tortellini" for the umpteenth time when the security guard suddenly clicked his ballpoint pen, clipped it to his shirt pocket and said curtly, "Wait here."

Now what? Where was he going? To keep my mind from racing, my attention turned to the line of Mexicans waiting to get in; a long line curled around the entrance like a sleeping serpent. My eyes settled on the lady stationed at the front of the line grasping a fat manila envelope. "How long have you been waiting?"

"Hmm . . . since five in the morning. A few hours."

"Is everybody in line waiting for the same thing?"

She looked around and shrugged. "For a visa? At least, that's what I'm here for." She pointed to her manila envelope.

"You're not mad?"

She shook her head and a slight grin broke across her face. "*Pues, no, señorita.*" Standing in a line for four or five hours; now that would make me furious. Not here. I was beginning to think standing in line was something of a national sport in Mexico.

Watching people wait in line for their visa reminded me of Marcelo, before he knew me and before he got his green card. He used to recall "his limbo lean years" when he'd go from job to job. He used to tell me how he even briefly folded and packed sweaters in a Brooklyn factory and washed dishes for a fine Italian restaurant before his green card finally arrived in the mail. "After waiting all that time for a green card," he'd say and pull out the card to show me, "it's pink."

My mind returned to the reality of waiting in front of the American Embassy. I tried to shake the iron bars a little, but, of course, nothing moved, but it still made me feel better. "Let me in . . . I poked my nose between the iron bars. "You pretentious pontifical peons . . ." I trailed off in midsentence when the same security guard reappeared.

"Here comes Smiley Face," I muttered. But this time, he had two fellow guards by his side. My initial feelings of fear and intimidation had vanished and were replaced with irritation.

"Do you have a letter from your news organization?" one of the new guards asked.

I rummaged through my bag and handed a phone number through the bars. "You can call my boss. He's the editor of the paper I work for, *The Observer*. See if he will help straighten this out." For some reason unknown to me, it took all three guards to scramble back to their cabin where they made a phone call.

It really wasn't my nature to argue with an embassy security guard. I mean, he had the international law on his side, not to mention a whistle-clean uniform and some very impressive law-enforcement tools around his belt. What did I have? A press badge and a theoretical appointment.

The security trio returned a few minutes later. The one who asked me all the questions fished for a key and slipped one into the keyhole of the gate, and said, "*Pasé.*"

"*Hmph!*" I marched past him, mumbling, "Surely the Mexican presidential house Los Pinos would be easier to get into."

The great iron gates screeched open and closed behind me with a clang. Once inside, I was feeling rather victorious until a different Mexican guard stopped me a few steps past the entrance where I had to explain in more detail the very same story. The guard eventually decided I wasn't dangerous so much as a pesky little reporter and motioned toward the nice neat rows of classroom chairs. "Wait here till someone comes to get you."

Seated on one of the wooden classroom chairs, I scribbled furiously about my unwelcome treatment in my notebook until an official escort came to whisk me away to pass through a metal detector. "You may go through," he said, waving his hand with authority. I plopped my canvas bag on the conveyor belt and stepped through the metal frame.

On the other side, another guard professionally poked at my keys, eye drops, honey cough drops, pens, and steno pads with his medical rubber gloves. "Just a lot of items," he noted with a voice of disappointment, as if he had expected to find a notebook that exploded or a pen housing a secret camera.

"Thanks." I grabbed my stuff and whispered, "Left my stink bomb at home."

Finally, finally, finally, I was inside the embassy walls. Already late for the meeting, I hurried past the grand fountain with its cascading waters and lush greenery to meet the officials from the Foreign Commercial Service. *Well, well, well. How ironic, I muttered, as I observed the majestic cascading waterfalls. I'm going to a conference on the scarcity of water.*

An hour later, I emerged from the water conference and felt that I had practiced the Good Neighbor Policy. I snagged a Mexican official for an impromptu interview in Spanish and conducted a brief interview with an American official in English afterwards. Spending two hours at a conference listening to a Neighborly Spat—My water is not your water— I still thought we had a long way to go to loving each other as good neighbors. After this American Embassy experience, I wasn't exactly singing "My country 'tis of thee, sweet land of liberty," if you know what I mean.

11

The Ghost of Frida Kahlo

T wo weeks after my embassy visit, the Toadess was housesitting. A bombshell blond named Kimberly blew in from New York and had just been hired at *The Observer*. Believe it or not, I found myself taking care of her house on Londres Street in exchange for peace and quiet. "Just call me Kimi," she told everybody in a babyish voice on her first day. The bombshell occasionally wrote features for the paper, though I never understood for what department or why. She seemed to float in and out of the newsroom. Somebody said it all made sense because she was wealthy and her father worked for the car industry in Mexico. Among the reporters, she was the only one who had a car in Mexico City besides Malena.

With considerable drama, she had summoned all of us plebian reporters to the parking lot.

"How do you like my brand, new Mustang?" she asked us, pointing with her long French, manicured nails to the long white stripe running down the middle.

"You drove this all the way from New York to Mexico City by yourself?" Dave asked.

"Yep. All by myself." She flipped her long blond hair to the other side of her shoulder.

My colleagues thought that was a fantastic feat. They goggled. I was the only one that found her New Yorker story hard to believe. I didn't mind confessing that her little driving adventure made me feel demoted since I came from New York by plane. Her beauty must have influenced their gullibility.

Meanwhile, everything else about this Kimi made me feel quite ugly, like a Toadess next to her.

Take her invitations, for example. Kimi invited the whole *Observer* staff to weekend pool parties in Cuernavaca, where her parents lived. I never went to those get-togethers because I heard they drank a lot and everybody ended up staying the night. I could not afford to lose a whole weekend or stand more than a minute listening to Kimi endlessly talk about Kimi.

But then an offer came that I couldn't refuse. Kimi announced she was going to Cancún with her boyfriend and asked if anyone was interested in house sitting for a week. My arm shot into the air. A whole house to myself in the suburbs away from slamming doors, shrieking kids, blasting ranchera music? Are you kidding? That is how I ended up at Kimi's place, sleeping in late on a Saturday morning in a very peaceful and leafy neighborhood called Coyoácan.

After getting out of bed on my own time, I got up only when I was hungry. I opened Kimi's refrigerator, not expecting to find anything except for a bottle of mineral water. Her fridge was surprisingly stacked with loaf of wheat bread, slices of bologna and ham, and an assortment of cheeses. Geez, I had been craving a meatball sandwich that I used to buy at a midtown deli in New York for a long time but making a sandwich from all of these fresh cold cuts would be the next best thing.

I quickly got to work. A few minutes later, a sandwich piled high with expensive lunchmeat, mayonnaise and yellow American cheese emerged from the pieces like a sculpture. A Mexican variation of the New York quintessential sandwich called a hero. I greedily took a big bite and nearly passed out from sheer blissful joy. I hadn't raided anybody's refrigerator since I was a teenager babysitting for the next-door neighbors. I justified my act with the fact that Kimi had a lot of money and could go to the butcher any old time she pleased. Maybe she even stocked the refrigerator for me, who knew?

After finishing my last morsel of sandwich, I threw open the house doors, inhaled the relatively clean air and looked around. The street was shockingly quiet and graced with gated homes. My eyes landed on a big blue house across the street. Who painted their house cobalt like that? Eccentric neighbors, obviously. I was curious so I wasted no time getting dressed and hurried across the street to find out. The house had a sign saying it was a museum of a painter. Not only that. It wasn't the house of any old painter but the house of Frida Kahlo. *The Blue House.* I was staying right across the street from the home of that famous Mexican artist! Here was my opportunity to visit the house of the artist who had those bushy awnings for eyebrows, the left brow running into the right brow. The unibrow was her trademark, but oh, what a threatening mustache she had.

I called Malena right away. I knew she would relish explaining Frida's art and teaching me about the place where Frida was born, lived, and died. I admit that I thought she was the know-it-all but at the same time, she would give me another perspective, doubling my appreciation for Frida. I was so thrilled when Malena said she'd come that I waited for her at the entrance of The Blue House for an hour. We paid the admission fee and joined a throng of tourists emptying buses and doing the same thing.

The house had two floors built around a courtyard with a beautiful, interior, maguey- cactus garden. We headed to Frida's bedroom, which displayed her famous bed with the mirror built into the top of the wooden canopy, the one she used to paint her reflection when she was bed-ridden. In fact, the whole house was full of more mirrors that the artist used to carefully inspect her own reflection—there were small mirrors and body-length mirrors everywhere.

One oil painting I particularly wanted to see was the one

that I had studied in Herrera's book Ashok had given me as a birthday gift. It was Frida's largest painting and one that she had created while going through her divorce from Diego. She called it *The Two Fridas.* Her painting showed two versions of herself, holding hands like a split personality. One Frida had a heart that was whole, the other an open-for-all-to-see broken heart with scissors in her hand to symbolize the severing of her relationship with Diego. I looked for that painting in the house and when we didn't find it, I turned to Malena, disappointed and said, "The painting, *The Two Fridas,* isn't here."

"You're right," Malena said, "I think it's in private hands."

As I continued going through the house, an avalanche of memories about my past relationship with Marcelo overwhelmed me. I let myself remember all of it for the first time in months. I stood there, eyes watering, when I saw the painting of a jagged cut of a watermelon, the last painting that Frida created before she died with an inscription *Viva la vida.* Long live life.

"What's the matter, *chica?* You don't like the watermelon painting?"

"No, that's not it."

"What is it? Something's wrong. You're sad."

"Nothing," I sniffed.

"How about going out to the garden again?" Malena asked. "The garden is the best part of the museum, anyway." We stepped out of the house into the greenery. "Come, let's sit."

We sat on a bench, among the vivid blues and yellow pyramid of the courtyard. Malena fished out a lighter from her purse, lit a cigarette with a flicker of her hand and with a deep inhale of cigarette, exhaled a trail of smoke. She leaned toward me. "Tell me."

I poured my heart out to Malena. I told her about Marcelo. How he had entered my life in college. How he was my first boyfriend. How I knew I was doomed the minute I laid eyes on him. He sat at a table in the center of the room, his eyes on me as I recited my poetry at a campus café in Ann Arbor. I couldn't keep my eyes off him either. So after the reading, he invited me to sit down and explain my favorite poem. To my surprise, Marcelo possessed sensitivity toward life, something that I thought the rest of the male species was born without. This mysterious thing called chemistry took me by surprise and I couldn't even begin to explain in a rational way. All I knew was that the insides of my thighs ached at the mere sight of him. When he took a sip of his coffee, I wished I were the coffee. I was jealous of his coffee cup. When he asked me out that evening, I nearly fell off my chair. A few months later, I graduated from college and moved to New York with him.

It was in our small New York apartment that I found Marcelo's monster, which had been hiding in the closet. He drank, and when he drank, he erupted like a volcano. He would stay out late in bars, and I'd wait up for him, half awake. Feeling helpless, the minute he came home, I'd ask him, "Where were you?" and he would fly into a rage.

"None of your God damn business."

Malena interrupted. "Wait, wait, wait a minute," Malena said, "Why did you stay with this bastard? Tell me why because I know you're a strong woman."

"I was scared."

"Scared? *You*?"

I nodded. "*Really* scared. He made me terrified. I was avoiding people. Blaming myself, having trouble sleeping. I'd get panic attacks when he'd come home."

"Okay, so you were traumatized by him. Go on."

"You won't believe this but I thought I was still in love with him. Even with his drinking problem and his temper."

"Crazy. He was wearing down your self-esteem, that's what it sounds like to me."

"Yeah, plus, I had no family nearby, except for my cousin Alex, but I didn't want to tell him because I was afraid of what he might say to Marcelo."

"What were you doing at the time? Were you writing? Working for a newspaper?" Malena asked.

"That was the other thing. We were so poor. Marcelo worked in a health clinic and I wrote for community newspapers. They paid me practically nothing. I felt stuck. I couldn't have paid for my own apartment."

"How did you finally get away from this guy?" Malena asked. "Did you finally leave him?"

"No, we had a fight."

I told Malena about the night Marcelo came home after a night of drinking and how he started throwing things around our apartment. Kicking the kitchen table and chairs. Denting the door. Smashing his fist against the wall. Threatening me. Saying he would kill me. This time, I was afraid his anger might turn physical on me. I panicked and picked up the phone.

"Don't you dare pick up that phone," he warned.

"I dialed 911 anyway and he stomped out the door. I hung up before anyone could answer."

"Wow, *chica*, you didn't even report him to the cops?"

"No. I had exactly twenty dollars in my purse. No credit cards. What could I do with that? I soon found out. Twenty dollars was like elastic, stretching into dinners and lunches and breakfasts of rice and coffee and coffee and rice for four weeks. I put on my only business suit and went to interview after interview until I landed the low-life copy editor's job in Manhattan."

"Hey, at least it paid the rent, *chica*," Malena said.

"Yeah, barely."

I continued to tell Malena how I then moved out of our apartment and into my own tiny studio in Queens. I admitted that the worst of it was I still wanted Marcelo back even though I knew he was an alcoholic and a raving maniac when he was drunk. A few weeks later, Marcelo found me in Queens and started phoning me, and I let him re-enter my life. The following two years I saw him off and on and agonized about how to make our relationship work, worrying about how to save him from the Poison in the Bottle. I told Malena how I surprised him at his work on Christmas by showing up with hot sauce and tamales and met *the wife*.

"*The wife*? You're kidding?"

"I wish I was."

"What did you do with the hot sauce and the tamales you were going to give to Marcelo?" Malena asked.

"What do you mean? I don't remember. I think I just dumped everything in a trash can."

Malena's eyes practically jumped out of her head. "You did what?"

"Who cares what I did with the stuff?"

"You dumped the stuff in a trash can?"

"I think that's what I did."

"You should have dumped it over *the wife's* head. That's what I would've done."

"I should of."

"I would have kicked him in the balls."

"I should of."

"Never mind. You shouldn't have brought that jerk anything, period. He didn't deserve a drop of hot sauce. Anyway, I'm going to teach you how to make the real chile sauce. Homemade."

"That would be great," I said. I knew she was trying to distract me.

"You'll love it. You'll see. It'll be good for your cooking repertoire and for your self-esteem. Just as long as you keep my recipe secret. ¡*Hecho*? Deal?"

"*Hecho*."

All of a sudden, we realized we were back in Frida Kahlo's garden. I sniffled because I had no more tears left. Malena looked drained from hearing my story. We stood up and she gave me a bear hug. "You want to go now?"

"Not yet, "I said. "I want to walk around for a while."

"Okay. Well, if that's the case, let's walk to the other end of garden and then we'll get out of here," Malena said. "Walking *will* make us feel better. Now, I want to ask you something, have you ever read Frida's diary?"

"No, why?"

"You should. Talk about suffering. Besides having an unfaithful man, Frida was in a trolley accident that left her with a broken spine, ribs and legs. She wrote in her diary that she had two accidents in her life, 'the trolley and meeting Diego Rivera.'"

"Oh, yeah, I know about the trolley accident."

Malena said that from her diary entries, her letters and biography, Frida's life with Diego seemed pretty bleak. Malena believed if Diego's three wives had ever met, there would have been a competition. "They would compete for whoever suffered the most."

"Wait a minute. Diego Rivera had three wives?" I asked.

"Yep. You ready to take a look at Wife Number One?"

"Ready. Let's see your impersonation."

With her hands on her hips, Malena's low raspy voice went a couple of octaves higher, her interpretation of a Russian-born painter. "He cheated on me and abandoned me in Paris, and that's just the beginning." It wasn't funny at all but somehow, I managed a smile.

"Wait till you see Wife Number Two," Malena went on with a fiercer voice to imitate her. "My story is even sadder. I was left with two small children. When he cheated on me, I wanted to grind up a pre-Columbian statue and feed it to him in his soup."

I was blowing my nose and feeling a little better already. "Okay, and then there was Frida?"

"Right," Malena said. "Frida. She'd show her painting *A Few Small Nips*. Frida supposedly painted this to show how much she was suffering from Diego. Do you know this painting?"

"No, is it morbid?"

"Bloody. A woman is lying on white sheets, splattered in blood after repeated stabs from a man standing over her with a knife in his hand. Frida painted the gruesome scene to show her pain over Diego's affair with Cristina. Her sister! No wonder Frida Kahlo wrote in her diary about Diego, "You've been my comrade, my fellow artist, and my best friend, but you've never been my husband."

"Wow, you're right. She really did suffer."

"You better believe it," Malena said. "After Frida died, Diego married again."

"So Frida wins the Sufferfest in your eyes?"

"Of course, she does, *chica!*"

"Well, Frida never had a faithful husband in her lifetime, we know that, but she certainly has a lot of fans now, doesn't she?" I pointed to all the women and men pouring in from the main entrance. "Look at all these people. I bet they can relate to her somehow, in some weird personal way. Her ghost lives in many of us."

"You're right, this place is a royal tourist trap. But if Frida Kahlo were able to summon herself from the great art exhibit in the sky, I think she would be mortified to see her face plastered on mugs, posters and buttons. As for that Marcelo bastard, I'd like to wring that man's neck. I've had some lousy boyfriends too—maybe not as lousy as yours, but bad enough."

"You have?" Malena always seemed in total control and I doubted if she'd open up about any of those lousy boyfriends.

Sure enough, she turned around and said, "Let's get out of here. I need another cigarette." We headed for the exit. Spending a Saturday afternoon with Malena at The Blue House was exhausting and refreshing at the same time. Malena was really kind to listen to me spill my guts and to be supportive, too. I couldn't help but be happy that I got away from Marcelo. I was proud of myself for taking that huge risk in leaving my New York life behind, and I was finally able to accept the reality of our relationship. I had survived.

12

On the Campaign Trail

M exican presidential elections were but a few months away when Guido—without warning—took me off the general news beat and assigned me the political beat. He wanted me to cover the campaigns of all three presidential candidates. "You will be their official tail. Follow them around. Record what they say."

I panicked. "Guido, listen. I'm no Marie Curie of politics. When it comes to Mexican politics, I can't tell the PAN from the PRI from the PRD. The acronyms of the political parties sound like the Greek alphabet."

"You'll learn as you go."

He didn't seem to be listening very carefully. I went on. "The political candidates? They all look and act the same. I'm serious. Left leaning, center standing, right tilting. I can't tell them apart. And I know zero about the way you elect officials here. Let alone the president. Even in the U.S., all I know is there are three branches of government, that's it."

"You're the hardest worker I have right now. I've decided that Kimi will be covering the general news and cultural beat from now on. Like I said, you'll learn as you go."

"No, I really can't learn. I can't." I was on the verge of throwing a tantrum. "You don't understand . . ." I muttered, watching him disappear down the hallway to his office. What about my tickets? The flash of free tickets hovering above, suspended by wires, dancing the cha cha cha and singing "no more of these, ha ha ha." Oh, how I'd miss covering cultural events. They fell into the general news beat, with it, I received press tickets to the theater shows, the chamber concerts, and the art openings. If these sweet tickets were going to go to Kimi, my social life would be reduced to fifteen degrees below zero. "Is there a little something extra for doing this?" I asked Guido when he came out later to check on an article in the newsroom.

"What do you mean?"

"A pay raise for example?"

"No, just a lot more work."

"Listen, Guido, remember what happened when I wrote the story on the Mexican-American War?"

"You mean your major screw-up? Of course."

"Well, it'll be much, much worse. Guaranteed. Your reputation as an editor will be ruined in no time by my reportorial mistakes. You want that to happen?"

Guido motioned my fears away. "This is different. I'll take the chance on you. Look at it this way, it'll give you a chance to repair your damaged reputation. Have you ever thought of that?"

I thought it over for a whole two seconds. Okay, he had a point. My current reporter status was the size of a chiclet square of gum. That didn't mean I could do this. I knew I couldn't do it. Mexican politicians are just so . . . so political.

"This," Guido was saying, as if he were doing me a favor, "is an opportunity that doesn't come along every day." He turned and disappeared again but this time, calling over his shoulder, "We only vote for a new president every six years."

"See what I mean?" I babbled to myself like an idiot and dropped in a chair in disbelief, "See that? I didn't even know that. That Mexicans elect a president every six years . . . we elect our president every four years, not six . . . See how clueless I am?"

Texan Dave was working alongside me at his computer. He shot me a look, shook his head. "Looks like someone's shitting in their shoes."

"Yeah, you better believe I am. Now what am I going to do?"

"Couldn't say." Dave went back to working without another word. With no sympathy on the colleague end, I started plotting how I could be taken off the political beat. I needed to do something drastic. Leap off the Latin American Tower? Jaywalk in traffic on Reforma Boulevard? Whatever I was going to do, I needed to do it right away.

A rational thought suddenly occurred to me. Ashok. I should call him for a job. He was working at an international wire service and I'd beg him for a job. Yes, that's what I would do. I dialed and plunged directly into my phone conversation by telling him that I was desperate and needed to talk to him personally.

At three o'clock, we met at La Café Habana. This cafe used to be one of our favorite hangouts when we were going out. We used to end up talking there for hours after browsing the city's bookstores. Rumor was Fidel Castro and Che Guevara planned the Cuban Revolution in this very cafe. At the moment, it was perfect. I was scheming for a political coup, how to get out of covering presidential elections.

Ashok calmly sipped a cup of herbal tea while I emptied a strong cup of espresso and told him about my stroke of injustice. "Guido knows I hate politics. Dave, the Texan, doesn't even care what he covers. Meanwhile, Kimi gets all the good stuff 'cause she's beautiful. Why would he do this to me?" I shoved my empty espresso cup to the edge of the table. I knew Ashok would understand because when he was writing for *The Observer*, he had covered everything from politics to the Mexican stock market to worker strikes. "I just can't cover Mexico politics."

"Hey, I know you're disappointed, but look at the bright

side."

"What? What bright side?"

"The PRI gives you amazing free breakfasts at their headquarters, Of course, they're scheduled at 7:00 a.m., and you're forced to read their official political statements," he said. "But I can still taste the chilaquiles bathed in green salsa. Toast. Fresh orange juice."

I wanted to give him a poke in the eyeballs. "This isn't funny. Can't you see I'm slipping on a reporter's banana skin?" I ordered my second cup of espresso.

"Sara, listen, could you be overreacting a bit?"

I could see there was no sympathy coming from Ashok, either. "You don't understand. I have a bad reputation to live down. This isn't the way to do it."

I drained my second cup of espresso. Ashok studied me.

He had these little stars in his pupils.

"I forgot how beautiful your mouth is," Ashok murmured.

His twinkling eyes were distracting me from my frightening new political assignment. I felt tiny bumps rising along my arms. "I haven't forgotten yours."

"I remember your kisses, too." He shifted in his chair and his knee bumped against mine accidentally on purpose. He must have sensed the exchange of heat for he leaned closer, his body sprawled practically across the table.

I leaned away from him, alarmed. "I need a new job right now, Ashok. This is horrible."

Once I said that, he straightened himself up in his chair and his warm voice had turned to iced tea. "Well, there's no opening at the wire service right now, but you'll be the first to call if someone leaves."

"Thanks, Ashok. I know I have to mature. Let's face it. When your boss tells you to do something that is clearly outside of your cognitive capabilities, you have to do it anyway."

"That's right. It'll be fine."

He jumped up and mumbled something about needing to get back to his office. As he walked out, I wanted to cling to his leg so he could drag me along but I settled for a clutch of the arm. "I hope you rescue me from the rip currents of Mexican politics. Please, Ashok. Remember me when you have a job opening."

"I will, I will, don't worry," he said, struggling to get past me. "I will call you when an opening comes up."

"Before I have a coronary?"

He nodded. "Before. Promise."

I released my grip of terror.

"In the meantime, try to enjoy the Mexican breakfasts."

Breakfasts? Who cared about that? It was hopeless. No one was going to rescue me from the hell hole of Mexican politics. Not Guido. Not Dave. Not even Ashok. No one.

The next morning, I had to get up very, very, very early, which to me, resulted in cruel and unusual punishment. I wasn't even on my way to a free *chilaquiles*-in-green-salsa-breakfast like Ashok had fondly recalled. I was bumping along on a press bus to a garbage dump, and the muffler was rattling loud enough to make it impossible to speak to the journalist next to me.

The press bus was following the presidential candidate of the ruling party, Miguel Castillo, and his bus rolled along a road to the outskirts of town, about an hour outside the city. There I was riding behind him, following him as the "official tail."

The bus lurched forward and rumbled through the gates. We clamored off the bus and I practically fell flat on my face from the odor. It smelled rotten. Something like the No. #7 train in August when the air-conditioning was out of whack.

I surveyed the garbage dump before me. The Great Plains of Plastic.

Mounds of waste spilled out—and it was the size of a lake. Torn plastic bags—pink, blue, yellow and white, piled up along with cigarette butts, dog poop, oil filters, broken pipe, filthy rags, strewn paper, rubber tires, soda cans, used syringes, rotten food, tin cans, deflated soccer balls, cardboard, broken glass, coat hangers and unrecognizable paraphernalia.

Shacks of corrugated tin were built in the trash heaps.

People were living in the tin shacks. *The garbage dump was their home.* A thought crossed my mind: I had better write at *least* ten inches about this.

When the photographers scrambled off the bus, and took one look at the dump, they went wild snapping pictures of the heaps of garbage. What a photo opportunity. Journalists love to record the poor of Mexico. If you squinted and took in the big picture, you could see a landfill with workers looking distant and small like ants. It was sobering.

"Mexico isn't for the meek and mild," I whispered. *"Mexico isn't for the meek and mild."*

Since this was a little campaign stop, off we went in a little journalistic convoy, trudging down the muddy lane on the tracks of Castillo. An *Observer* photographer and I stopped on the dirt trail to observe a family sifting through garbage. I wanted to talk to the woman bent over the garbage heaps picking through the debris. She appeared to be plucking away, little by little, as if she were picking cotton. She was plucking a plastic bottle, an aluminum can and a copper wire from the waste heap and depositing these in her garbage bags. Her children were playing on towers of plastic bottles.

The Observer photographer snapped photos of the children and then disappeared with the rest of the group. Meanwhile, I stayed in the same spot in a daze, watching her at work. I wanted to ask the woman gripping a garbage bag and a stick if she were the mother of the children. I whipped out my notebook and asked. Luckily, she said yes.

Then I asked her if I could ask a few questions about her family's living conditions.

She nodded.

"Do you have running water or a bathroom?"

The mother with the missing teeth said no. My skin prickled.

"What about your children?"

"My children," she told me, "were born in the garbage dump. When someone leaves cars, we fix them and use them. When there aren't any, we walk to the nearest store and get some basic food."

"What do you do for water?"

"Drink *pulque*."

My first impulse was to upchuck the sweet bread and coffee I had for breakfast. *Pulque* is a fermented and very strong alcoholic drink made from maguey. "Drink *pulque* for water." I was trying to focus on the facts and note this in my notebook, but my gut wanted to retch.

"The children drink soda," she added.

Write this down, Sara. It's important. The mother told me that her entire family had left the state of Durango many years before to look for better living conditions in the Mexican capital.

My pen rested, and I looked up to study the woman's wind-beaten face. I didn't know where Durango was. I was afraid to ask her if she felt her family had a better life here, compared to Durango but I knew I had to. "How is your life different from Durango?"

"Much worse," she said. "Much, much worse here," and she turned away to resume poking at the mounds of plastic bottles. Her voice trailed off. "All the rest of my family is still in Durango."

This dump reeked of poverty and I was taking notes on it? What kind of reporter was I? A lucky one. That's what. Yes, I was a lucky, lucky lady. Thankful for my noisy apartment in The Ruins. Thankful for my peso-pinching job. Thankful for pinto beans and rice on the table every day. Oh, the kind of survival skills families must need here to live.

"You are a survivor," I said to the mother. "Did you know that?"

"While there is struggle, there is life, and while there is life, there is struggle," she said while continuing to pick through the trash.

Wow. As poor as she is, she had a message of hope. She had just repeated a common Mexican refrain. The woman reminded me of the inner strength Mexicans have when they face tough times.

If only I had half of that strength, I thought. But I am a survivor of sorts, too. An emotional survivor. I survived Marcelo's alcoholism, his rages. And now in Mexico, I am surviving on my own in a foreign country.

By this time, Guido's voice ran through my brain like a scratched record, "Follow them around. Be their official tails." Okay. It was true. I came to this landfill to cover the presidential candidate, Castillo. It was *not* to cover poverty. But I had to ask one more question to the mother. "How do you make money for your family from sorting garbage?"

She motioned to the mounds of rubble. "Metal. Plastic. Glass. People use them all again. We sell it all."

I waved some very aggressive flies away from my face. "Okay, one last question, I promise. Do you—"

"Hey, wasn't that your bus that you came on?" the mother asked as her eyes settled on something behind me.

I spun around. The buses were gone. No one but the garbage pickers sorting through the trash. Castillo and the press had vanished. "Hey, where is everybody? I didn't hear anything." I looked up the road. In the distance, a dark dot was fast diminishing. The second I realized that the buses had left me at the landfill, I broke out in a run for my life, chasing after the moving dot and screamed like a lunatic "Stop! Stop the bus! Wait for me!" When the speck disappeared, I stopped running down the dirt road.

Great! That's just great. They left me here! My ride back to town. Now, what?

I returned to the dump, to the very spot I had been interviewing the mother. She was gone. Maybe I could find her and she'd help me. I scanned the landfill. There were clusters of garbage pickers far in the distance. I didn't see her in that group. She must have moved to a different territory.

Kreee kree kree. A flock of pigeons descended near my feet. *Kreee kree kree.* Pigeons gathered by my toes, pecking, hopping and flapping around my feet. *Kreee kree kree.* "What is this? An important pigeon meeting? Are you deciding where to eat and poop next? Get out of here! *Shoo, shoo, shoo!*"

I needed to phone someone fast. This was an emergency. A taxi. The garbage dump was an hour away from anything resembling city life. That's the only way to get back. I'll call Guido too. Tell him that the bus left without me. Oh, I could just hear his voice. "Follow them around. Be their tails. Record everything they say." On second thought, maybe I shouldn't call Guido.

I dialed the taxi company. As it was ringing, I thought I don't really have money for this taxi. I'll have to use my credit card. "Oh, hello, Sara Tortellini here, and I'd like to schedule a pick-up at the garbage dump. Which garbage dump? Um . . .Your guess was as good as mine."

The dispatcher hung up on me.

The pigeons had crept closer to me again. They were at my feet. A few of those scavengers swooped overhead.

"You guys have no sense of personal space, do you?" I said. I kicked my foot out in an attempt to get the ones around my feet to fly away.

The flock of birds flapped at me, and one flew closer to my head. *Kak kak kak kyow.*

I ducked.

Kak kak kak kyow.

"Okay, so I'm invading your little hang-out. Too bad."

I dialed the cab company again. I explained my situation again. A sketchy garbage dump an hour away? No.

Wait. There's something else. I had to color the truth a bit here and there, just to get taxi driver to come. In my *pobrecito* Spanish. I told him that I was involved in the news business, not the waste disposal business. I had a deadline to meet. And, as a famous foreign correspondent, I was reporting on *the haves* versus *the have-nots* for a highly respected newsmagazine in the States and I needed to inform the public. And did he know that I was up for a journalism award? Didn't he want to be a part of this epoch-making event and possibly the journalism prize of the century? No, I wasn't making the whole thing up.

Where? Where am I you ask? Hee-hee. That's a good question. Wait. Don't hang up on me this time. You know, the biggest dump of the city? No? Where? Um . . . let's see. Where they're building new concrete houses and what'shisname, that political guy, you know, the guy running for president, the PRI guy, Castillo? Yeah, that's his name, thanks. Yeah, well, anyway, where Castillo is taking credit for the concrete houses built for the garbage pickers? Yeah, that's where I am. No, I'm not a garbage collector, I just told you, I am a famous foreign correspondent. What are your beady little eyes watching me for? No, that wasn't for you, señor, taxista. I was talking to these scruffy little—never mind." I went on until I was blueberry in the face.

When I got off the phone, I stepped in a pile of pigeon poo.

"Thanks. Just what the doctor ordered. My shoes need to be fertilized."

Kreee kree kree.

"You know what I'm going to do?" The tension must have gotten to me. I was talking to pigeons out loud. "Find a huge hawk to eat you guys alive. You just wait."

I walked to the outside of the dump and leaned against the gate. Will the driver even come like he said he would on the phone? Will he be able to find the right place?

An hour later, the cab driver showed up. He was a boy who looked about fifteen years old in a gypsy cab, but I didn't care. He had reached the dump without an address and found me waiting outside the gate. I was very, very grateful to him. After riding with him for about a half hour, though, I was getting worried about the fare so I asked him to leave me off at the nearest Metro station, and I'd find my way back to the city from there. One subway and two buses later, I crawled into the newsroom on my last legs.

I would pretend nothing happened. I would just sit down in a calm sort of way and fill a certain number of newsprint inches and meet a deadline without anybody knowing what an awful terrible no-good day I had. But first, I had to hunt down Malena, whom I knew had a small stash of hair supplies and toiletries. Carrying an armful of supplies, to the bathroom I went to wash my hands and clean my shoes of the pigeon poo.

Then I applied an entire ozone layer of hairspray to mask the stench of the garbage dump, sniffing the air around me. "Hmm . . . Me smell so much better now."

Coming out of the bathroom and sauntering back to the newsroom to write about the garbage picker family, a familiar voice caught me off guard.

"Heard you got left."

It was Guido.

"Oh, you wouldn't believe my morning, Guido. There was this family—"

"Rafael, the photographer, told me. You were talking to a family on the dump the whole time. You couldn't hear the sound of the buses starting up?"

"Oh, Guido, the mom drinks pulque and the kids drink Coke instead of water."

"Do I look like I run the Bleeding Hearts Club to you?"

I shook my head. I thought he was going to pop those veins on his short neck.

"You weren't following the presidential candidate Castillo."

"Ah . . . I was kind of following him."

"What did I tell you when I put you on the campaign yesterday? That was only yesterday."

"Um . . . you said to follow the candidates around. Be their tail. Record everything they say."

"That's right. That's what I said. But did you listen? You did not."

"I just had a soft spot for the mother, that's all."

"So I have a soft spot for Coca Cola in the morning. For beautiful women with big butts. For a cold Modelo beer after work. Does that mean I write a news story about them?"

"No." My shoulders drooped a little.

"Our readers don't need enlightenment, Sara. They need campaign coverage. Got it?"

"Got it."

Guido shook his head and disappeared down the hallway mumbling, "I'm trying to run a newspaper."

So I went back to the newsroom and wrote about the

garbage pickers, how they're getting cement houses to replace their tin shacks—all because of that PRI what's-his-name—the one who wants to be the president—gave them the money. That was the political article that Guido wanted me to write. I called it the Campbell's canned soup version. Then I wrote another story on the mother raising her family on a garbage dump. I wrote and wrote and wrote until I had cramps in my hand and wrist by the time I was done. It was my very first human feature story.

I knew Guido would never publish it in *The Observer*, of course, but I thought I'd try to submit it to more left-leaning, less governmentally-tilted kind of publication in the future. Okay, my subversive story wasn't on the level of Jacob Riis, who documented the condition of the New York City tenements in *How the Other Half Lives*, but I wrote a deeper story than my usual news factoids. I was positive it came from deep within the heart. On the other hand, it only built on my reputation as a rookie reporter. In fact, now I had to be really careful. I didn't want to give Guido another reason to fire me.

Whew! If this was only the first campaign stop, I could tell I was in for some tough times. I would face rigorous conditions on this political beat. I would need combat boots.

* * *

A few days later, I continued to feel inadequate and unsure of myself, but was on my way to trail the left-leaning political candidate Felipe Solís. A scarf wrapped around my mouth protected me from the nasty air molecules outside. The oxygen was shaping into solid particles. Ironically, or maybe not so ironically, the leftist candidate Solís was scheduled to speak on the measures he would take to reduce pollution if elected. How about talking about today, with a zero percent chance of a Popo sighting? El Popo is the volcano Popocatépetl that lies southeast of the city and people from the capital use this as a barometer for the day's pollution. They always say that if I could see El Popo, the air couldn't be that bad.

Oh, but it was bad. All the way to the press conference, I was reminded of how bad. Walking to the Metro station, I spotted VW Beetles scuttle about the street like cucarachas sputtering a trail of fumes on me. It was like being sprayed with a RAID can. Cars rattled by with exhaust systems hacking like a chain smoker. A city bus belched by as I crossed the street, and I dodged the exhaust cloud. The air was yellow and, in some parts, even brown, a putrid brown. "It's like living in a bowl—a toilet bowl," a taxi driver once told me. "You have no choice. The smoke, the dust, the dirt. You're mixed up in it." I was mixed up in it, that's for sure. We were in a valley surrounded by mountains and there was no way of escaping that geographical fact.

People born in this city, *chilangos*, were immune to being frightened by pollution. They're tough. Even if the solid particles were forming burritos, enchiladas, and tostadas in the air and might crash to the ground, they denied the seriousness of it. Take Malena, for example. She had comforted me the first few months that I had complained about it. "Don't worry, there aren't any burritos, enchiladas and tostadas forming up there," she assured me. "They're birds. Finches."

"Of course, they're finches," I had said. "What about the finches that have asthmatic attacks in midair that I've heard about?"

"Yes, there are those. They drop from the sky–just step over them on the sidewalks."

Or Enrique, who was also born in this city. He was worse than Malena in terms of comforting me about the pollution.

"Don't think of the yellow haze that sets over the city as pollution. Think of it as maybe the gold dust of some great past civilization," he had said. "Like the gold dust of the Aztec society."

"Wow, I'd need some kind of imagination to think of it that way," I had told him.

"It's not hard to do. Picture the atmosphere carrying the very air that Montezuma inhaled in his royal lungs. Or even Cuauhtémoc."

"Right," I deeply inhaled and sucked in a mouthful of fumes while trying to imagine these great Aztec royals waving the royal wave at the crowds and inflating their lungs, but I started coughing.

"It sort of makes you want to treat the pollution with more respect, doesn't it?"

"No, Enrique, it doesn't." I said, shaking my head. "Not for me." He laughed.

I squinted skyward. No finches in midair that I could see. All I saw were corpulent clouds the color of oatmeal. They were changing color, and a blustery wind was swirling. "Looks like rain!" I said as I descended into the underground station and not a minute too soon. Charcoal drops began to splash from the sky. When it rained on a polluted day, the drops changed shape and color and fell in bits of solids like snowflakes. But were black. Smogflakes.

* * *

An hour later, on my way home from the Solís pollution conference and coming out of the Metro, when the smogflakes I had dodged earlier turned into a run-for-your-life downpour. Nine long blocks to go before I arrived home. Wouldn't you know it? After days of faithfully taking my New York umbrella with me during the rainy season, I had accidentally left it at home. Man, I would have to buy another umbrella or get soaked by sooty rain. I should buy another one.

The hunt for a new umbrella began. I had no clue what kind of store sold umbrellas in Mexico. In New York, Puerto Ricans were the umbrella men. They stood on the street corners, dressed in their bright yellow plastic ponchos, a bucket of folded umbrellas at their feet, shouting in the rain, "*¡Umbras! ¡Umbras!*" to all of us pedestrians squishing by. Needless to say, when people were dripping and shivering, those twenty-five dollar umbrellas flew out of their buckets like flying carpets. That's how I became the owner of my black umbrella sitting uselessly at home.

I scanned the street corners. Nobody was standing on them selling umbrellas and calling out *umbras*, so I darted into shops asking for an *umbra*. Into the stationery store. Into the pharmacy. Into the convenience store, the Oxxo store. No *umbras* for sale. Every time I asked the store clerks if they had an *umbra*, they looked at me like I had gone bonkers. They brushed me off, *no se vende aquí*—they aren't sold here.

Cold and wet, I returned to the streets with my shoulders slumped and my eyes fixed on the ground to avoid stepping in puddles, talking aloud to myself just like homeless people do on street corners in New York: I can't believe that no one is carrying an umbrella . . .They aren't even racing to the nearest awning, or bolting into stores like maniacs . . . They don't seem to be the least disturbed they are getting wet . . . a dirty wet . . . Maybe I'm overreacting . . . Are Mexicans waterproof? Do fat drops of rain roll off their skin and their shoulders to keep them magically dry while I'm here squeaking in my shoes?

Shivering, I trudged on. Still, I wasn't about to give up on buying an umbrella. I dipped into a stationery store one more time. Inside, the lady appeared horrified that I was dripping on her floor so I hurried it up and asked for a sheet of brown paper as fast as I could. She gave me a dirty look. But before she could *shoo-shoo,* I drew a kindergarten picture of an umbrella on my steno pad and pointed to my sketch and asked the clerk what the word for that object was.

"*El paraguas*," her finger pounced on my drawing.

"Umbrella?"

"Sí,"

"Not *umbras*?"

"¿*Qué*?"

"That's what this is called?" I poked at my crudely drawn umbrella again.

"Yes, and we don't have any. No hay."

An umbrella was called el paraguas. Oh. I realized then that those Puerto Rican umbrella men were simply cutting off the English ending of "umbrellas" to make it "umbras" and it was their fault I'd been traipsing around the city making a fool of myself. That wasn't even the Spanish word for it, doofus.

"Where can I get one?" I continued. "One of those paraguas?"

"¿Quién sabe? Who knows?"

"Do Mexicans normally buy umbrellas?"

"Puede ser. Could be."

"Does it usually rain this hard?"

She raised her shoulders up and down. "Si Dios quiere . . . If God wills it."

My soggy appearance and persistence must have inspired a molecule of compassion at that point because the lady suddenly pulled out industrial scissors and a giant roll of plastic. She whacked off a huge sheet, cut out a large hole for my head, and thrust the plastic in my face. She sputtered away in broken English. "Here, take it, free, I give you umbrella, free!"

My stiff and cold fingers lifted the plastic sheet out of her hands and over my head. "Oh, thank you. How much do I owe you?"

"It work. Rain. Go," she said in English.

"I want to pay you for it, though. How much do I owe you?"

"You take, go, freeeee," she said waving me away.

"Thank you, *señora*, I mean, *muy amable*." Very kind. I stumbled out of the stationery store to the hammering of the rain.

It was at that moment, as charcoal raindrops bounced off my head like Little League baseballs, that a light bulb flashed. I had finally discovered the correct name for what I was looking for, el paraguas, I discovered people seldom carry one here, or maybe not at all. The Mexican umbrella was a page torn from the daily newspaper held over your head or a sheet of plastic with a hole in it. I wore my Mexican umbrella for the last two blocks home.

I reached my apartment sloshing in my shoes. Wet as I was, I was happy to have the rain wash away the pollution so we could breathe clean air, even for a short while.

13

Secret Ballots

Ojo!" Guido said, pointing his two fingers to his eyes and pulling down the corner of his right eye. "Watch everybody very carefully for any cheating."

"You see?" I said, pointing my two fingers at my eyes in a V. "You're talking to Miss Hawk Eyes."

It was Election Day. I would technically be done covering presidential candidates after this voting day. Hopefully, Guido would let me return to the general news beat. This political beat had turned into a post-war Marshall Plan for me to rebuild my damaged reputation as a reporter and prove to Guido that I possessed serious Fourth Estate skills.

Guido sent Miss Hawk Eyes to a "high risk" polling station. I sat right next to the officials handing out ballots and guarding the ballot boxes. I was on the lookout for cheaters. I mean, if there were any, I'd certainly find them. I had no idea what happened if you were caught cheating, except it had to be something bad.

All day long my eyes were glued to a man who stained voters' thumbs yellow with ink. This was so voters couldn't vote twice. Not a sign of any shenanigans, not a single one. It was so boring, in fact, you could have heard a thud every now and then from me dozing off and falling face flat to the floor, only to get up and prop my face up with giant toothpicks like Salvador Dali's painting *Sleep*.

When the polls closed, I joined about a million other people, pushing and shoving to get a tiny place to stand outside the Interior Secretariat building to wait for a preliminary vote count.

The first signs of trouble surfaced when no vote count came. Hours passed. Night fell. We were ushered inside an auditorium to wait while security men wearing dark suits whispered code names into their walkie-talkies.

Still not a dribble of news on who was ahead in the race.

Nothing happened until a few minutes before midnight. A spokesperson for the Interior Secretariat suddenly appeared on stage and walked briskly to the microphone stand.

"We have a slight problem . . . (clearing of throat) tonight. It seems that . . . (another clearing of throat) the ballot counting machine . . . (third clearing of throat) has crashed."

The computer crashed? What? My ears had fallen off my head and bounced across the floor.

"At this time, we have no more information," the official declared.

A deep murmur rippled through the crowd when he said this. The official shuffled his papers nervously, lifted them off the podium, and was about to disappear. Nobody asked questions. Did they even want to know? Wasn't it our duty as the press to ask hard-nosed questions?

Sara Tortellini had questions. Sara *who?* You know who, the *Almost Fired Sara*, who up to this point, was successfully recovering her reputation as a credible reporter and didn't want to flush it down the toilet over one silly question. But I had a question.

As soon as the government spokesman walked across the stage, my hand sprouted in the air. I shook my hand hard so he would call on me. I shook it this way, and that way, every which way.

The press official stopped in his tracks and nodded in my direction to proceed with my question.

"Could you *at least* tell us which candidate was in the lead, based on a preliminary vote count, before the computer broke down?"

"No, uh . . . not . . . uh . . . at this time." The official deflated before my eyes. It reminded me of when I rode over a nail and the air hissed out of my bicycle tire.

Hands sprouted in the air and shook every which way, covering the auditorium like a canopy of palm trees in the Amazon rainforest. My question caused a chain reaction.

The official ignored the hands, the questions, and kept on walking.

"When will the computer be up and running again?" somebody shouted.

"No questions at this time!" His voice rose.

"What time did the machine stop running?" somebody else yelled at him.

"No more questions!" The face of the press official turned purple. A clear sign when someone's trying to hide something. A person's face turns all kinds of weird colors.

Then he disappeared behind the curtain.

A stunned press stared at the empty stage. The public address system announced the auditorium would be closing, effective immediately and *to please leave*. We shuffled out.

All I could think about on the way home was I was robbed of my glory without a front-page story announcing a newly elected president. Instead, I'd write a about a long wait at the Interior Secretariat and a computer crash.

The next day, Castillo announced himself the winner. He was president. He offered no vote count or numbers to support his claim that he had beat his rivals. Only a very large number of rapid eye blinks and throat clearings in his five-minute speech.

A week later, Castillo called the press together again to announce how he won 50.36 percent of the vote. A hairbreadth margin. What a *sneaky* victory. Genetically engineered. While I was on the lookout for people voting twice at the ballot box, I had never dreamed that the government could do wholesale tinkering with the ballot counting machine.

Whew! I was so glad it was over. From dawn to dusk, day after day, I battled a billion balloons, banners and boisterous crowds. If Hillary Clinton logged 112 countries hopping around the earth as Secretary of State, I bet my Frequent Footer points could beat her Frequent Flier points. Attending 564 rallies in the presidential campaign, I survived mobs of people elbowing me in the ribs, stepping on my toes and shouting so loud that I still have ringing in my ears. I had survived my deployment in the combat zone.

I was done. Cut loose, gone with the wind, as in *finito*. With my bag slung over my shoulder, I dashed through the corridors, pushing past people and racing down the stairs to the exit door. In my excitement, I missed one of the steps and went thumping down the steps to land on the floor in a thud. On my rump with my legs in the air. All I could think of was thank God I was wearing pants. No one saw my underwear.

A face appeared, hovering. "You still in one piece?"

"I don't know yet." My eyes landed on the stranger who had a press credential dangling from his neck and one on his backpack. A fellow reporter. He stretched his hand. "Let me help you up."

I leaned my weight into his hand and stood up. "Thanks."

"How do you feel?"

I dusted myself off. "Not sure yet."

The man had a flowing tousled mop. "It looks like you took a pretty hard fall."

"Yeah, now I feel it."

"Check to see if you have all your pieces. I mean, you look like you do, I mean, good, considering the circumstances."

"A bit banged up, that's all. I don't know how I did that. I wasn't thinking. I mean, I *was* thinking. Just about other things." My eyes fell on his mesmerizing cocoa-bean eyes. "I'm okay."

"Hello, then!" he said.

"Hello." The living male specimen before me had a very square jaw . . . and was smoldering handsome—handsome enough to melt my eyeballs.

"Hmm . . .You look vaguely familiar." he said, this time in a perfect English enunciation.

"Familiar as in a fly-by before a crash landing?"

"No, that's not it."

I began gathering my pencils and cough drops and my scarf from the floor. "So I noticed you're speaking English very well."

He snapped his fingers. "That's it! I know. Aren't you the reporter that asked for the vote count on election night?"

"That's me."

"I thought so."

"By the way, you don't look familiar at all." I said when reaching for my steno pad strewn on the floor.

He swiped my steno pad off the floor before I could get to it. "The voting count question. Naive, I must say, but brave."

That accent of his. Crispy-fried-bacon kind of English. This time, mysteriously, I found his accent lovely. I wondered if he knew any quotes from Will Shakespeare. "Naïve, huh?"

"Very."

"It's called The Fourth Estate. So you speak British English?"

"I do. From my years living in London. But I like Spanish better," he said and winked at me.

"Well, I need to practice my Spanish so I should be speaking in Spanish anyway."

"Gringa?"

I nodded.

"If I may ask," the Mexican guy went on but changed into Spanish.

"Again? Another question? Who's full of questions today?"

"Where were you off to in such a hurry? I mean, two minutes ago, you were at the press conference."

What press conference? Wow. Running out of a press

conference seemed a million miles away. We gazed at each other and laughed for no reason. I had just witnessed the main candidate declare the final vote count, and it was already half-forgotten. I turned to ask the male specimen who stood before me, "What did you think happened back there?"

"You mean the slim victory Castillo had just announced?"

"Yes."

"You want to know what I really think?" he asked.

I nodded and pretended I was listening when I really wasn't. I started walking toward the Metro station and the male specimen fell in step. His wide mouth was distracting like mine, and when he spoke, his words were elegant, even in Spanish. What should I do with the British English? I decided that I would think about that later. "Yeah, what do you think?" I asked him again.

"I think that A Very Hungry Computer must have been eating away at Solís' margin of victory somewhere inside the building a week ago."

I only heard the last part of his sentence. "That's what I think! We couldn't very well accuse a computer of stealing ballots, could we?"

"No, we couldn't. Votes for the leftist candidate Solís were probably pouring in faster than the Very Hungry Computer could digest them," said the Mexican reporter with the silver tongue, wide mouth and long hair.

"If the Hungry Computer got a horrible case of indigestion and broke down," I said with excitement, "then nobody could point fingers, name names, and send anyone to jail!"

"¡Híjole! (Oh, my God!) You understand a lot about the Mexican political system for a gringa."

"I do? Tell that to my boss! Hey, what's your name, anyway?"

"José, I work for El Universal. Fifteen years."

"Sara, a hack from *The Observer*. A year and half."

14

A Romantic Plunge

I know, I know. I know better. I promised myself not to get near any male if I felt my pulse skipping beats. As soon as I met José, I got that feeling. I needed to run the other way. Smoke alarms went off. Sirens flashed. Chinese gongs vibrated. With his sculpted jaw, penetrating gaze, wavy mop of hair, José was irresistible. But he did have a major flaw. He swam in the same gene pool as Marcelo. As Ashok. As Francisco. I had sworn off *all men*. Still, I was madly attracted to José. Of course, before I'd consider getting involved in a relationship again, that little inner voice that I had been arguing with for so long was telling me I needed to examine my own situation. I dug out my Marlboro pack of cigarettes and reviewed the *"Warning:* EVACUATION: MEN ARE FATAL HAZARDS TO YOUR HEALTH" that I had been carrying around in my purse.

I had been in Mexico a full year and a half and I had failed in my earlier attempts to heal my heart. Expecting a miracle from the Virgin failed to work, and my short-lived romantic interlude with Ashok failed to help me forget my relationship with Marcelo. As for a fling with my young tutor Francisco, it had entered my mind but there was no way because he was too young. If a miracle and a stab at romance couldn't do it, I didn't know what could. Should I force myself to go out with other people to get over Marcelo? There it was again. My mother's voice bounced off my eardrums. "What about that nice Mark Goldstein? He's an insurance executive and lives in Grosse Pointe now. He always asks about you."

I put away the cigarette pack with the warning, thinking it over. I will not have a rerun of a bad relationship. What about your loneliness, Sara? True. I am so lonely I hold meaningful conversations with my coffee cup. On the other hand, why would I want to make my life more complicated? Why couldn't I just enjoy the infatuation with the television newscaster from *Univision*, Jorge Campos? He was perfect. He reports from Miami two-thousand miles away and is unreachable.

I then I had an epiphany.

Forget newscaster crush, my heart thumped for the close-up kind.

A few days after meeting him on the steps, José asked me out. We didn't go out on a date exactly. Instead of going to that famous restaurant he suggested, we went around and around Chapultepec Park while I acted like a police detective from a criminal investigation unit from New York, NCIS. Battle-hardened, I had a list of questions to ruthlessly interrogate José before he set foot in my heart's territory.

"Do you have a wife stashed in some hidden pocket?"

"No," he answered in a rumbly, soothing voice that could put a newborn baby to sleep.

How would I know for sure there wasn't another woman somewhere hidden? I would need to ask him point blank. "Could I arrive any old time at your house and check if somebody else is living there?"

"Yes." He laughed. "You come up with the weirdest questions."

"Are you afraid of the "M" word?"

"What?"

I had to explain the "M" word. No, it didn't stand for

Mexico, but was an American euphemism for Marriage as in "getting married." I explained that for most men in the U.S. that I had met, the mere mention of the word sent many of his species scurrying away. Was he afraid of that? In other words, was he a Commitment Phobe?"

"No."

"Do you live with your mother? Do you enjoy eating her cooking? Are you looking for another cook? Or laundry lady?" Hee-hee, this to check if he was a Mama's boy.

"No, not really."

"Aha! This is where it became a bit tricky. I went on for another twenty minutes before two questionable pieces of evidence emerged: his age, he was in his late 30s. And two, his mother happened to live in the apartment right above him. I couldn't decide if a grown man living ten feet away from his mom disqualified him. These bits of information definitely tilted toward a possible "Mama's Boy." But I wasn't sure if this was normal in Mexico. Who knew, so I thought and thought before finally deciding that there wasn't enough evidence to dismiss him just for that.

Since both of those facts were minor incriminating bits of evidence, I would reconsider in the future if more evidence came up. For now, I pictured him shirtless when I was looking at him and it took all my discipline to concentrate on the questions. I resolved to give him a chance.

I put away my notebook. It was all settled.

We went out on a real date after that. Each date resembled an old-fashioned courting ritual rather than the usual sitting around the apartment and listening to music without spending a single peso as I had with Ashok. It beat browsing stale and stuffy old bookstores on Saturdays, which I occasionally still did with Ashok. With José, I was going out to nice places and nothing was work-related. José opened doors for me, pulled out chairs like a gentleman. He had a charm that exuded from every pore. He took me to the fine hacienda restaurant in San Angel for *tacos al pastor*. These tacos were made of marinated pork shaved off a spit. It was a Mexican tradition to eat them on Sundays, and something I had been wanting to try. We were building our relationship on friendship, but of course there was a tiny voice inside me begging, "Give me more. More, please!"

Before I could add any new excitement to the relationship department, I took *The Observer* elevator to the ground floor and knocked at the in-house doctor's door. "Come in, Sara," said Dr. Ignacio, opening the door wide. "I haven't seen you in quite some time."

"Yeah, thank goodness," I remarked, recalling when I was the revolving door for his treatment for my amoebas when I first arrived.

He laughed, and after I signed in, he took me into his consultation room right away. "What brings you in for a visit today?"

"Well, I'm paranoid about getting pregnant, and well, um . . . the birth control pills that I've tried in the States all made me sick. And I don't really trust condoms."

"I see. You want to try something different?"

"But it has to be 100%. Like the pills. No 5% failure rate or anything, like those latex objects. I mean condoms. There must be some surefire and trouble-free method of protection?"

"There's Depo-Provera," Dr. Ignacio said. "It's a shot and it's made for people like you. Many Mexican women use this."

"What does it do?"

"It's 100% effective against pregnancy."

"What about the side effects?"

"None whatsoever."

"Hmm . . . how long does it last?"

"Three months."

"Three months?" Wow, I had never heard of this kind of birth control—but three months without hassles? Hard to believe that there were no side effects, but I decided to believe the doctor. After all, he was the doctor.

Doctor Ignacio pulled out his humongous needle and gave me a wallop of the hormones in an injection in my butt and BAAM! I was good for three months.

After the shot, it seemed like I was hungry all the time, and

I gained a few pounds. I was always worried about my weight but I dismissed the nagging presence of extra pounds and decided to give a try at love again. Even if I opened up my heart a crack, José had already shown he was fun to be with and he seemed to care about me. There must be something to that.

I struggled at letting myself experience a relationship again. One night after the movies, we went back to his house. We were having some tortillas smeared with smashed beans that José's mother had left for him.

I spooned some chile sauce on my rolled tortilla. "This chile sauce your mom makes, I have to admit, it's good."

"Any chile is good, if you ask me. It has the power to make your lips swell until they are so plump and kissable."

"Really?"

"Yeah. Look at your lips right now. They're cherrylicious red."

"They are not."

"Are too. Look in the mirror if you don't believe me," José said.

I went to the bathroom mirror and checked my lips. They were regular Sara lips, no big deal. Hee-hee, little did José know that what was inside my mouth, the Frenchy tongue, was the golden nugget that would make him crazy.

I came back to the table. "Same Sara lips if you ask me."

"Looking at those lips of yours, my heart goes *ba-bum, ba bum*," José said. He gently took my hand and put it on his heart. "Here, feel my heart."

"It *is* racing."

"And I get hot, too," Jose added. "You know, in the mood." He lifted my hand from his chest and put it on his crutch. "Feel it."

His lump grew in my hand and I let go.

"What?" José asked. "Why did you do that?"

"Eating oysters is supposed to make you hot, but I never heard of hot sauce working this way," I said, trying to take my mind off the electricity pulsating through my body.

"Swear it does. Produces endorphins." José said. "You feel it, I know you do, I know you're hot for me."

"Well, I want to learn how to make a good homemade chile sauce like your mom."

"You know that Montezuma used to drink hot chocolate spiked with chiles before visiting his concubines?" José asked.

"Now that's disgusting."

"Why do you find that disgusting?"

"Having many women and not being loyal to one?"

"Well, all I'm saying is that chiles can give a person the urge to tear off one's clothes."

I reached over to caress José's midnight hair, which hung loose and long, not gathered in his usual pony tail.

"See? I told you the chiles were working," he said.

I unbuttoned his shirt and took my index finger and made doodles on his chest."

"Hmm . . . could be. But who said I'm ready to tear off my clothing?"

He put down his tortilla. "Oh, *mamacita*. You're so sexy." He leaned over and gave me a wet kiss.

I was afraid that my heart would beat out of my chest. I pushed my plate away. "José, we need to talk. I don't want to get involved with another man. I'm not ready."

"Who says you have to be ready?" he whispered.

"I do." The very next instant, José's arms enveloped me. His lips wet my neck, his hands grabbed my butt from underneath my dress, and his body pressed against mine.

I pulled away again. "Listen. You don't understand. I had a bad experience. I haven't told you about it yet."

"Shh . . ." José pressed his velvety wine lips to my mouth and his two fingers slipped into my body. I was wet and burning. *Now* I wanted to tear off my clothing. I hadn't had a man in so long and I hadn't realized how much I was missing one until that moment.

"You want to tell me what happened with your last boyfriend?"

"Not *now*." What I wanted at the moment was to pull my

142

legs apart and slither away with him.

"Should we go to the bedroom?"

"Yeah, let's." I blew in his ear. Our entwined tangle of body parts stumbled to the bedroom and we fell on the bed. Fire burned between my legs.

José began removing my dress, my bra, and my panties piece by piece. I was fully naked and felt embarrassed because I was in the very spot where I didn't want to be.

He started blowing in my ear. "Let me not to the marriage of true minds, Admit impediments, Love is not love—"

"—You *do* know Shakespeare!" I didn't want him to think I was just another easy American woman, but he *did* know Shakespeare. I couldn't believe it.

"Which alters when it alteration finds . . ."

"Hmm . . ."

He kept blowing more words from that romantic bard in my ear. What an idiot I was. I didn't want a relationship again, didn't want the emotional intimacy. At the same time, I was panting and aching for him and José knew it.

"You're so beautiful," José was saying. "You have such a long, beautiful neck, like a swan."

"I do?" I felt self-conscious again. Seeing me totally naked and he notices my neck? That can't be good.

He fumbled to unzip his pants. I wanted him inside of me so bad. He looked up at me when he was fully naked and smiled. "Are you getting warmed up looking at me?"

"Hmm . . ." I just said even though he looked like a Greek statue.

"Feel it . . . see how it's been waiting for you?" My hands clasped his body again. He was warm, throbbing and hard as a rock. While I was rubbing him, my thighs were aching for him to enter me, but he didn't. He waited. He cupped my breasts in his hands and started lightly squeezing them. It felt so good that I wanted to scream. While he was swallowing my nipples in his mouth, I tried to distract myself. I remembered what Marcelo had told me during one of our lovemaking sessions. "There will only be one love in your life. After me, it will be all lust."

I didn't want lust, I wanted love. I didn't love José, I wanted sex. Remembering those words and Marcelo, a couple of tears dropped off my eyelashes. It wasn't until José rolled over on top of me and penetrated me, rotating, thrusting and covering my neck with saliva, that the sadness disappeared. The next thing I knew, I experienced a climax so intense that my nails dug into José's chest. I shrieked and he shrieked back that I was going to tear him apart. I almost did. But I didn't. While I lay on the bed in bliss, José continued to lick my ear, murmur, and nibble at my neck before he fell silent.

I'll never shower again, I thought.

* * *

"You know, you have some strange marks on your neck." Malena observed, when she saw me in newsroom the next day.

"I do?"

Malena dipped in her purse for a lipstick mirror and showed me my reflection.

My finger dabbed at the hickey bruises on my neck. My cheeks went hot. "You're right. I'll be more careful."

"*Sí, chica.* You're my *comadre*, my friend. I watch out for you." Malena pulled off the scarf from her neck. "Here, wear it for a couple of days."

"Thanks."

"Remember, we want romance, not vampires."

"Yeah, yeah, I got it."

"Who is he? Do I know him?"

He's a reporter from *El Universal*. Has long wavy hair. His name is José,"

"Hmm . . . don't think I do. *Cuidado, chica*, with the Vampire. He has to be a gentleman first, treat you with respect. Don't forget that."

"Oh, don't worry. It's not serious or anything."

After I went to bed with José that first time, I thought about it very carefully. Was this the beginning of getting really involved? If so, I didn't want to. I was scared of my feelings toward him. I called José and told him I needed some time away from him. That I wasn't going to the movies that evening.

"But I already bought the tickets. You wanted to see that movie so bad and they're only for tonight."

"I'm sorry, I can't go. I need some space, to think about everything."

"I'll give you a break afterwards, but only if you go to the movies with me tonight. Promise."

So we went to the movies. Then we went back to his house and made love again. It became a series of dates, romantic evenings, and he even whispered Shakespeare's sonnets sometimes in my ear when we were making love. My favorite was Sonnet 29. "When, in disgrace, with fortune and men's Eyes . . ." Oh, I couldn't get enough of José.

* * *

I was completely in the throes of my romantic rumble when cousin Alex came to visit Mexico a few weeks later. Well, I must admit, he didn't come to only visit *me*. He was stopping overnight in the city on his way to Cancún. He would be vacationing there with the longtime boyfriend so he called me to see if I could meet him at the airport and suggested that we do something together that night. I said I would not only meet him, but I had a surprise—José—for him.

Coming out of baggage claim, I spotted Alex but had forgotten how lanky and handsome my cousin was. He looked eight feet tall rolling his two huge pieces of luggage behind him.

"Hi, cuz," I said and opened my arms as he came close.

"Here I am, all the way from Noo Yawk City," he announced with considerable theatrical drama. I glanced at José. He had this look of surprise and his penetrating eyes were asking, "Why didn't tell you he was gay?"

I ignored his shocked expression and turned to my cousin. "I'm so glad to see you, cuz."

Alex bent his towering body for a hug and then whipped

open his black wool coat to give us a peek. "Look what I have hiding under here!"

He had a purple T-shirt on and skin-tight white shorts underneath.

"Oh, my God!" I laughed. "You're daring!"

"Oh, naughty, naughty!"

"Naughty is right," I said. I had never seen him act this way. I guess when you're born and raised in Michigan, coming to Mexico for vacation seemed exotic.

I shot a look at José. His eyebrows had risen.

"Don't worry," Alex went on. "I have the boringest shorts and a blando polo shirt in my bag. Or a Hawaiian shirt and looser pants. All in this little bag of mine." He patted the duffel. "I'll just keep everything—I mean—I'll just keep myself covered till I'm in Cancún."

"Be free, cuz. I love it when you stand out," I said.

Then I introduced him to José.

"So this is the mystery package you were talking about?" Alex gave José a head-to -toe sweep.

"And you're the cousin Sara has talked about—a lot," José said.

"We share a mutual endearment, don't we?" Alex said.

José nodded. I could almost see the long hairs on his head shrink and coil to his scalp. I immediately sensed they didn't like each other by their curt exchanges. But the intense dislike was confirmed when José picked up Alex's bag and said, "Just to warn you, we don't normally wear shorts on the streets in the capital. Only at the beaches."

Alex's eyebrows lifted. "Oh? Good to know."

On our way to the car, Alex stayed a few strides behind to whisper in my ear, "Long hair deceiving. Very conservative, straight as a ruler. Just a heads up."

We rode along in awkward silence. "What does your cousin do?" José asked me even though Alex was sitting in the back seat and could hear perfectly fine.

"Why don't you ask him?"

Alex stretched his hand from the back seat and wiggled his

fingers to show José in the front seat. "Ah, that would be me. Cousin here. I am indeed."

"Sorry," José mumbled. "What do you do?"

"I'm an account manager at an advertising agency. Don't ask me which one or any mundane details. I'm here on vacation."

"Nice job. Do you like working there?"

"How about a little radio?" Alex suddenly asked.

José shrugged. "Sure." He switched on the radio to a station playing Mexican pop.

"*Psst*. Sara?" Alex whispered in my ear from the back seat. I turned around. He tugged at the tiny dark hairs of his own head, and in a low voice said. "Just like me. Military crew cut? See that? *Hee-hee*. Very deceiving."

After a brief and extremely polite dinner together in the Hotel Majestic's restaurant, we asked Alex if he wanted us to show him around the city.

"Go out?" he said in horror. "In this city?"

That's when I noticed his slur in his speech. I sensed he had been drinking on the plane because when I hugged him at the airport, I smelled his breath. Plus, he had ordered shots of tequila over dinner.

"Not me," Alex slurred.

"Why not?" José asked.

He wiggled his index finger in the air. "For one thing, I need my beauty rest." He stuck another finger in the air. "Number two. This metropolis, I mean this mega . . . mega . . . ga . . . polis is kind of sketchy. This isn't Cancún."

"Aw . . . come on," José said. "You just have to be careful. There are bad guys in New York, too."

"No, really. I have to get up early. Cancún. The hotel will call a taxi for the airport. At some wee hour. Tomorrow morning, I mean."

I could see José's eyes narrow. "You can't compare New York, a city of eight million, to a city of twenty million in the same breath."

"José, he just said he doesn't want to go out."

Alex gazed at me across the table. "Right, Sara. I really do need my beauty rest."

"Well, then . . ." I hesitated, and rose from my seat. "We won't keep you from going to bed."

José and Alex stood up and shook hands, politely.

My cousin looked at me carefully, as if fully seeing me for the first time that evening. "Tell me the Tortellini truth. You like living here?"

"I do."

He looked at me with suspicious eyes.

"Honestly, Alex. I do."

"Well, I worry about you, Sara. Every time I talk to you on the phone, you tell me how forgotten you are by the family. How lonely you are."

"My fatal flaw. Don't worry about me, Alex. I'm fine. The only thing is . . . I miss you." I fell into his long arms for a wraparound hug and lingered. I whispered in his ear, "So how do you like José?"

"Hmm . . ." He waved the palm of his hand sideways. That was Tortellini code for a couple of notches below a "so-so."

I got a pit in my stomach. I hugged him again and wanted to show him how he was a part of me. He gave me a gentle poke in the back. "Er . . . unclench your wrestler grip, please."

"Oh, sorry," and then I added, "I love you, Alex."

"Me, too," he said, and stumbled into the elevator, wiggling his fingers slightly in a bye as the doors snapped shut.

José turned to me. "Wow," he said, "you mean that's who you're closest to in your family?"

"Yep, that's who," I said, not wanting to explain things. I could not help thinking of Alex suffering with cancer by himself in New York. I felt guilty. He had always been there for me, and I wasn't there for him in his illness.

"Now I understand why you're in Mexico," he said.

I ignored the remark and turned toward the hotel's exit. "Can you take me home?"

"Sure. That was a stupid thing to say, wasn't it?"

I didn't say anything.

"You know I care about you," José said.

"Care? That's how you express 'care'?" I snapped. "Let's go."

I wasn't going to get into a discussion about us at the moment. Whether or not I loved José, I couldn't really say. I loved his shoulder length wavy hair and I loved his hypnotizing chocolate eyes. We had a lot of common interests. I loved the sex we had. I realized after my cousin's reaction to José that indeed I must have liked José more than I realized. I felt like defending him. Maybe too much. Maybe I was feeling more about José than I wanted to admit, maybe I wanted him to "love" me more than "care about" me.

Push serious thoughts away, push, push them away. I forced myself not to think about our relationship in a deeper way. After all, I was having fun with him, wasn't I? Haven't I been too serious before? I was Princess Lust-a-Lot and enjoying it.

* * *

One Saturday morning, not long after Alex's visit, we were two sex-starved maniacs going at it. José was giving me mouth-to-mouth resuscitation as if I were dead when Ashok arrived.

At the knock on the door, I yelled, "Coming!" I threw my clothes on, and swung open the door.

"Hi, Ashok," I said in a daze.

"Hello, Sara," Ashok said, handing me a book. "I came to return *Pedro Páramo.*"

"Oh." I felt my body parts were scattered around the house. I was trying to find a right hip here and left thigh there and put them back in place while struggling to engage in a coherent conversation with Ashok at the same time. "Did you like it?"

"It was a good read. I'd love to get your thoughts on it."

"Sounds good."

"I was in the neighborhood and wondered if you wanted to check out the bookshops with me."

I shot a glance at the bedroom door and my voice dropped. "I don't think I can do that right now."

The light in Ashok's face faded and was replaced with puzzlement. "Ahm, okay. No problem. Ahm . . . well . . . then . . . thanks again for lending me the book," he said as he turned to walk away.

"Um . . .Ashok." I called after him. I shot another glance at the bedroom and opened the door a bit wider. I figured, what the heck, I was dressed already and wasn't going back to the bed anytime soon. "Um . . . you can come in for a second and I'll make some coffee."

"Oh, that would be great." He stepped in and sat in a kitchen chair. "But I can't stay."

"Who is it, Sara?" José yelled from the bedroom.

Ashok popped out of his chair like a Jack-in-the-Box. "Gotta go."

"It's Ashok. A co-worker stopped by," I called out, and motioned for him to sit down again.

José rushed out of the bedroom with his pants unzipped, his hair bunched up in a tangled mop and bare chested. "Your co-worker? I've never met him."

He thrust out his hand at Ashok as if he were brandishing a sword in a duel. "José Murano, and you are?"

Ashok extended his hand as if he were offering Jose´a vegetable paring knife. "Ashok Sharma." He paused. His eyes darted to me and then back at José. "Just stopped by to return a book to Sara. On my way to browse the bookshops right now. Sara suggested a quick cup of coffee first."

José shot me a nasty glance.

I gave him a dirty look back and motioned to him to zip up his pants.

"You and Sara work together?"

"Used to. Sara's great. Fine journalist. Side by side, we saw the world's defects," Ashok said.

"Really," José said in a sarcastic tone. "Side by side?"

"Well, I must be—"

"You saw each other every day?" José asked. "I mean, you said, side by side."

A mysterious grin appeared on Ashok's face, as if he were

suddenly enjoying the exchange with José. "Every day?" He scratched his two-whiskered chin. "Let me see, was it every day, Sara?" Ashok shot me another glance.

I made a slashing motion across my throat to stop talking.

Ashok went on. "I wouldn't say every day, would you, Sara? No."

"We used to work different hours, José," I added.

"But if we were to think deeply about it, Sara, I guess we did see each other every day. Yes. yes. For a few brief hours only. And when we did, we worked side by side."

"Oh, really," José said.

"Really," Ashok replied, edging closer to the door.

"Really?" José asked, and shot me a you're-dead-look.

Time to step in. "How about some *Nescafe* coffee everyone? The water is boiling right now."

"No, I must run, Sara," Ashok said.

"Sure?"

"He's sure," José said.

Ashok dropped a quick "Nice meeting you" to José and was off.

Once the door closed, José turned and said in a very loud voice marked with suspicion: "What are you doing with this guy?"

"For God's sake, José, he was my co-worker. It's different."

"Why different?"

"We worked together, and he's a friend."

"Oh? Now he's not only your co-worker but now he's your friend too?"

"Well, I've known him a little over a year and a half. Since I've been in Mexico. But now he works somewhere else. For a wire service. Not to worry."

"Why didn't you tell me that? That this boyfriend of yours knows you better than I do?"

"Oh, come on, you're not jealous, are you?"

"What—Jealous! Jealous? Of him?"

"Because we worked together?"

"You didn't just work at the same place. You worked *side by side.* You saw the world's defects together."

"That's what reporters do when they work in the newsroom. You should know. You work for *El Universal.* Don't you work with your co-workers? Why are you making such a big deal of it?"

"He's your friend. You said so yourself."

Thank God I didn't tell him that Ashok and I used to go out.

"Why would I be jealous? Of Mr. Guru who knows you better than I do?"

"I didn't say that. I said he's known me *longer,* not *better.*"

"I'm not jealous."

"You're not?"

The tips of my fingers glided lightly over his chest.

"Okay, just a little."

"Can we just drop this subject and have some coffee now?"

"Maybe. Maybe not. He knew where you lived, didn't he? He must have been over here before. You shared a book together. What else do you share together?"

Oh, I could see that José was flippity jealous. When I saw him like that for the first time, it was like throwing a cup of cold water in my face. Suddenly, I noticed that he had slight acne scars, which I hadn't noticed before, but I couldn't help but notice them at that moment—and I wanted to forget about it, but I thought they looked ugly.

* * *

Our romance—Sara, acting like Ms. Slotsky—went on for a couple of months, but after meeting Ashok, José gradually started changing. The majestic language of Cervantes that he spoke when he first went out was turning into a loose cannon of suggestive jokes. From his tongue, the most ordinary expressions began to take on sexual meaning.

"Are you ready?" I asked him when I had finished putting on my makeup and was getting my sweater to leave for a concert.

"Let's go then," he said, pointing with his chin to the bed.

When the phone rang, and I was on my way to answer it, I'd say, "I'm coming!"

He'd call out after me, "But I haven't even warmed you up." It was tiresome and I told him so, but he didn't stop.

He kept on using lots of words with double meanings, which are called albures in Spanish, but it was a mortifying trip to the market that became the fateful blow. José had a car and we would go food shopping together once a week. Buying the groceries from lots of little shops in the city had turned out to be a time-consuming process and the novelty of it had long worn off, so I was glad to get our own weekly groceries all in one place.

"Look at this mango! And cheap!" I squealed, excited that had found a ripe mango for a fraction of the price I'd pay for it in New York.

"You've got two ripe ones!" he cooed and held two mangoes against his chest.

"Pleeeease." I pushed the shopping basket past him to the dairy section. "I need eggs and milk," I said and opened a carton of eggs to inspect if they were broken.

"Why? When you can have mine?" he glanced around the store to see if someone was looking and since nobody was, clutched his crotch.

"That's gross." My face puckered into dozens of cracks and crannies. "Why did you do that?"

"Well," he said, "why not?" He always seemed clueless when his joking offended me.

"Would you please stop? Go away." He followed me around the store in silence the rest of the shopping trip. I paid for my groceries. He paid for his. When we got to the car, I opened the trunk and began to load the grocery bags.

"I'll put it in," José said, rushing over to help me, "I know you like it when I put it in."

I slid into the car. I couldn't, for the life of me, see the humor in that. Who did he think he was, an obnoxious twelve-year-old trying to be funny? How could he have changed so drastically or was this the real José? "You need to grow up," I told him.

As we rode along, I was thinking about those Shakespearean sonnets that he whispered into my ear while making love. At first, I thought they were romantic until I found out they were really not. They were bawdy, full of sexual puns, and I learned Shakespeare was one horny and frustrated dude.

"Do you know what the whole trouble with you is?" Jóse was asking. A three-second pause. He continued. "You're too serious. You need me. You need someone like me. I'm lighter, funnier. My jokes are perfect."

"You know what we call remarks like yours in English?" I asked him. "Do you know? Adolescent humor, that's what, and your jokes are disgusting."

"Really?"

"Definitely. Are you going to act like you are a twelve-year old all your life?"

"That isn't funny."

Our ride was strained. I knew perfectly well that in Mexico even cars and driving maneuvers could be interpreted in a sexual way. Start her up, warm her up. Even when José looked me up and down as if he were feasting. He no longer said, "You look beautiful." Instead, he'd say, "Your butt turns me on."

"Get it?" José winked. Actually, I hadn't even heard what he had just said. So then he winked again. "Get it?"

I couldn't "get it" anymore. Get what? That all he cared about was our physical relationship? That the only way he looked at me was not as a whole woman with many needs, but a woman to have sex with on a regular basis? I didn't know what our relationship was about and I was tired of analyzing everything. Was I expecting too much? Confused, was I feeling too deeply about him and heading toward disaster again?

During that ride home, there was silence in the car. To me, it seemed like a really loud silence, like a public announcement that we weren't going to make it together. Before my inner critic started jabbering away, I told myself I was glad to have had the time with José. Before our relationship, I was wondering if I had to amputate my heart, which was not getting any blood flow as a result of staying frozen from my heartbreak. With José, I realized I did regain some feeling in my heart.

Still all the romantics on the planet couldn't convince me that there was a true love out there somewhere for me. I remained cynical. It was clear that I needed more healing.

I'd have to find another way to heal this palpitating human heart of mine.

15

Pues, Doctorcita . . .

Not long after breaking up with José, I woke up with an ache under my arm. The first thing I did was ignore it for as long as possible. Then a few days later, a lump appeared in my left breast. This made me feel so bad I wracked my brains trying to figure out what caused all this.

Did I do twenty-five push-ups all of a sudden to get in shape? *No.*

Did I spend a night throwing around a fourteen-pound ball at the local bowling alley? *No.*

Did I lift another 5-kilo bag of oranges from the farmer's market? *No.*

Nothing like that, at least nothing that I could remember.

Until I remembered. The ache in the armpit began shortly after the birth control shot at the newspaper clinic. Yeah, that's when I noticed it for the first time. The lump in my breast? New.

Weeks went by. The ache in my armpit grew. The lump grew. Pretty soon, I couldn't even sleep on my left side. At night, I pulled a blanket over my face, wishing everything would go away. But it wasn't the kind of problem that would just go away by itself. So I tried ice, heat, massage—I even drank a whole bottle of cough syrup, but three days later, I woke up from my codeine-induced coma and still in pain.

It wasn't until my lump reached the size of a golf ball that I seized Malena at work and buried my face in her shoulder like a baby. I told her everything, including the whiny part, "I'm afraid of going to a Mexican doctor."

After hugging me tight, Malena peeled me off her shoulder and led by the hand into the restroom. "Let me see that thing."

I lifted my arm and directed her fingers to the lump. "Feel it? "

"*¡Híjole!*" It's so big and hard. You need to go to a doctor like *now*." Her eyes were wide and serious-looking.

"Yeah, but what doctor?"

"A gynecologist for starters. Don't worry, *chica*. I'll give you the name of mine. She's good."

Wouldn't you know it, a socially prominent person like Malena referred me, and I was given an appointment with her gynecologist in a top-notch hospital the very next day.

"A fear-inspired brain wave brought me here," I told the doctor.

"I'm glad you came," she said.

After she heard my symptoms, she referred me to a cancer doctor.

Within a few days, I was meeting Dr. Marta, the oncologist, whose jet-black hair was threaded with grey strands and pulled into a tight bun. She introduced herself in flawless English. I was glad about her beautiful English because I knew I couldn't complain properly in my linguistically impaired Spanish.

"I have got a big problem, Doctor," I said, sticking my middle finger into my armpit, "it hurts here," and smooshing the lump on my breast, "and here."

"How long have you noticed the soreness under your arm?"

"A while . . ." My eyes swam with tears.

"How long?"

"Hard to say, I was trying to ignore it . . . it didn't hurt at first . . . a few months?"

The clucking sound of disapproval. "Why did you wait so long?

"I don't know. I was just trying to . . ." I stopped myself and looked up at the ceiling. I wasn't about to tell her that I was terrified of being treated by a foreign doctor. Of getting weighed at the doctor's, even if the scale told me my weight in kilos. Of getting any illness other than a cold.

"Do you realize, Sara," the doctor began, "that we might be looking at surgery?"

I nodded.

"Do you realize," the doctor continued, "that it could be malignant?"

My head bobbed again.

"I'll order a biopsy right away."

Biopsy? Did she say biopsy? At that moment, I felt exactly the way Dorothy must have felt when she realized all she really wanted to do was to go back to Kansas.

Before I could get out of there, I was taken to another room for the biopsy, and the test showed that the lump was very big, and very fibrous. Whether it was malignant or not, Dr. Marta was uncertain.

"Hmm . . ." she looked up from her clipboard, gazing at me with tenderness and asked, "Have you ever thought about having kids?"

"Um . . . well . . . actually . . . I was in love with this guy . . ." Wait a minute! How did that question all of a sudden open a dam of emotions that came swooshing through the floodgates? Up until then, I was making heroic efforts to be brave and strong but then and there, I started to unravel. Driveling on about Marcelo secretly marrying someone else, *not me*, and if that wasn't bad enough, I had always wanted to get married and have kids right out of college, and here I was in Mexico, with a pain in my armpit and a lump in my boobie.

She patted my knee and held on to my shoulder until I collected myself. "Do you have a family member here in Mexico?"

I shook my head.

She pulled a tissue from the box next to the sink and stood very still next to me. "You'll be able to face this, I know you will."

"I'm not ready to die yet," I said, wiping my nose.

"Listen. You're getting a lump removed. There's a good chance it will be benign. I believe you'll feel better afterwards."

"Okay." I nodded, not fully recovered from answering the question about kids. It had hit upon something in me, deep down inside.

"Are you ready for this?" she asked.

I reached for another tissue. "Not really, I mean . . ." I glimpsed at the Dr. Marta. She gave me a smile that warmed me inside, and suddenly, I felt protected and cared for. "I guess I have to be."

"Good. Now I want you to find a friend to bring you to the hospital the day of the operation and someone to take you home the next day, okay? You will be staying overnight."

"Thank you, doctor. I'm glad I found you," I said.

As soon as I got home, I called Malena to tell her everything, and she simply said. "You're going to be okay, Sara. You got me. Now go get me a taco to digest all this news."

The morning of the surgery, I carefully gathered all my important papers: my social security card, driver's license, birth certificate and telephone numbers of everybody I had ever known in my life and put them in a little bag. Then I waited for Malena to come and pick me up. When she arrived, I handed her my "life bag."

"You're not worried at all, are you?" Malena asked, examining my written instructions on what to do and who to contact in case of my death.

"I haven't told my parents. Or Alex."

"Your choice, *chica*. Today, let me do the worrying for you, okay?"

I nodded, glad to hand over even a smidgen of worry to someone else.

Right before the operation, I had to sign off on the

possibility of having my breast removed if the growth were found malignant during the operation. Only then would the doctor decide whether it was necessary.

As the nurse wheeled me down the hallway into the operating room, I called out to Malena. "Fingers crossed, knock on wood, and say as many prayers you can. Don't forget to let the Virgin know, too!"

"I will, I will, "Malena called out, "don't worry so much, *chica.* I'm sending up all my prayers!" And she gave me an air kiss.

Dr. Marta and an anesthesiologist were waiting for me in the operating room and classical music was playing. The next thing I knew I had slept through the surgery and was waking up in the recovery room.

Still a little groggy, Dr. Marta came in, and asked me how I felt.

"Is my breast still there?" I asked in the foggy tone of voice you use when someone is coming out of anesthesia.

"Yes, and we got all the tumor out. Non-cancerous."

I heaved a sigh of relief. And then I go to touch my breasts and noticed my whole chest was encased in a box of plaster. What's *this?*"

"Protection for your breasts."

I gently knocked at my hard shell. *"Man.* I didn't know I was going to have *this.* My two lovely ladies were seriously tucked away. I mean, they weren't encased in a jewelry box. They were buried in a box large enough to hold a microwave oven.

"The protection must cover your entire chest," Dr. Marta explained.

"Both breasts?"

"It's temporary," the doctor reassured me. We can't just protect *one.* We need to make it look, uh . . . balanced."

A smile spread over my face. With this huge plaster cast, I felt like my breasts were at least size 40 DDD. "How long do I get to be Dolly Parton?"

"Two and a half weeks," she answered. "By the way, who's

Dolly Parton?"

* * *

Early the next morning, Malena came to pick me up. "Chica, how are you feeling?"

"Relieved. It wasn't cancerous and I still have both breasts. Look!" I pointed to my chest, "I can't see 'em or touch 'em so I really don't know if both boobies are in there, but I think they are."

She furrowed her brows and pointed to my box of plaster. "Geez, that's some armor of protection there."

"How does it look?" I asked.

"Like the breastplate of Xena the Warrior."

A smile broke across my face. "I have to wear loose dresses to cover it up."

"To hide your big mamas?"

"Right."

"You should be showing them off, darling."

"Plaster isn't sexy."

"You've got a point. Let's get you dressed."

Before I could sit up to dress, José suddenly appeared in the doorway of my hospital room.

"Well, look who's here. Prince Charming himself," Malena said.

"Hi, Sara."

"*You?* Where did you come from?"

"Is that a hello?"

"Sorry. Hi."

He continued to gaze at me from the doorway.

"Come in," Malena said. "Statues have no warmth."

"Seriously, José. How did you find out I was here?"

"Oh, I have surveillance at a distance."

"That sounds creepy."

"Don't worry. I said it was from a distance."

"I mean it. How did you find out?"

"Malena called me."

"Called *you?*

My eyebrows rose and I shot a glance at Malena.

She nodded.

José said, "Don't look so shocked."

"It's just that . . . I thought she didn't . . . like you."

Malena cleared her throat to remind us she was standing right there.

He gazed at Malena. "I think that still might be the case. She may have called because she thought *you* might like to see me."

"Hmm . . ."

"Okay, you two. I'm just outside in the hallway," Malena said, and slipped through the doorway.

An awkward silence.

José edged closer to the bed, bent over, and looked deep in my eyes. "How are you feeling?"

"Still enjoying the anesthesia." I knocked on my chest. "Hard as a rock."

"Are you in pain?"

"No, groggy. Just relieved it's not cancerous."

"I'm glad to hear it's benign, too. Here," he said, and handed a wrapped package from behind his back. "Just a little something to cheer you up."

"Now I'm starting to feel like an invalid." I unwrapped the package. It was a pashmina shawl. The perfect blue, not navy and not baby blue, but somewhere in between. My favorite blue.

"I didn't bring you flowers 'cause I know they remind you of funerals. I hope you like the color."

"It's beautiful."

At that moment, the doctor came in.

"Well, I'm off to work, Sara," José said. He bent down, gave me a kiss on the cheek and whispered something in my ear.

"Thanks, José. It was thoughtful of you to come."

The doctor gave me a prescription for some painkillers.

"*Pues, doctorcita, gracias por todo.*" Thanks, doctor, for everything.

"You're welcome. Don't forget your check-up in a week

and a half."

After Malena helped me get out of bed, we headed slowly toward the hospital's accounting office. Walking arm and arm with Malena, I shuffled along the corridor and was thinking how I had overcome the fear of being treated by a Mexican doctor and having surgery in a foreign country. The first-rate female oncologist and the hospital staff had given me quality care. To top it all off, in order to pay for the operation, the hospital officials gave me a reasonable payment plan for one year. I couldn't wait to call Mom and Alex and tell them how everything went well.

"Hold on a minute, Malena." We stopped so I could take a breath and sit down for a few minutes. "All right, I want to know why you called José."

"I thought he would want to know about your operation, that's all. I didn't tell him to come to the hospital. He asked for the name of the hospital, though."

"You know he whispered goodbye."

"What do you mean?"

He told me, "'Parting is such sweet sorrow.'"

"Why did he say that? To make you fall for the Shakespeare stuff again?"

"To tell me goodbye. Remember? We didn't end too well. That was his way of saying goodbye."

"You're not falling for him again, are you?"

"No, not again, but aren't you surprised he never said a word about my big boobies? No jokes whatsoever. Didn't ask to touch my plaster chest, either."

"Yeah, so unlike him, huh? How long do you think that will last?"

"You're probably right. Before you know it, he'll be pointing to his vital appendage."

* * *

Three days passed and still sporting my voluptuous bosom of plaster, I returned to work and to my part-time job as an

English language teacher at a private language academy in the Tepeyac neighborhood. A few months earlier, I had started to supplement my meager salary at *The Observer* by teaching English classes to young Mexican girls training to be bilingual secretaries. I worked three hours in the early morning twice a week and then headed over to the newspaper.

"The past tense!" I shouted at the class of girls. "That's the most important—we must work on irregular verbs in the past tense."

For students at the intermediate level, the past tense was a pressing need. Otherwise, they were stuck in the perpetual present. "Show me your fine set of teeth when you say the verbs," I said to my students, who didn't say a word about their teacher going from a 34B when she left for a three-day vacation to a 40 DDD when she came back.

A hand shot up.

"Yes?"

"*Maestra,*" said an earnest-looking student with doe-like eyes. "When you say the verbs in the past tense, you look mean. Like you're mad at us." Giggles.

"That's because my jaw has dropped. English growls."

More giggles.

"Now you can show us how to use "brought" correctly in a sentence," I told her.

The earnest student replied promptly, "I brought to the class all my books." As usual, I decided to ignore her mangled word order because when most of her sentence was correct, it was a victory for both of us. Plus, I wasn't feeling all that well on painkillers and antibiotics that I had been prescribed after the operation. I was still recovering and my stomach was jumping.

After the verb pronunciation exercises, I moved on to a structured writing practice. "Write three grammatically correct sentences," I instructed them as I assigned three irregular verbs to each student.

Their brows wrinkled, they pursed their lips, and faraway stares clouded their faces. Some of them even scratched their heads. Others flipped through their small dictionaries. They were good students and I felt badly that I couldn't give them all of my energy. The medicine I was taking for pain made me want to puke and made my head light.

Suddenly, out of nowhere, the walls swayed. The windows quivered. My head went light. "Class, I think I'm getting sick," I announced and grabbed the edges of their desks to make my way back to the teacher's desk to sit down.

SHOOKA SHOOKA-desks vibrated. Books shimmied off the desks and KA-BOOM, KA-BOOM crashed to the floor. Backpacks slid SSSHHHHHH, SSSSS across the room and THUDOOM slammed into the wall.

Screams erupted. "*Maestra! Terremoto!*" Earthquake!

We fled to the doorframe of our classroom like startled rabbits. "*¡A la puerta!* Go to the door! *¡Vaya a la puerta!*" More students shrieked as they leaped from their seats and raced to the door. I froze in my chair until a student pushed me to the door. As we huddled under the door frame, each elbowing for enough space. I fleetingly wondered if my students had noticed my plaster shell of a chest. My students hugged me against my rock hard bust but didn't say a word.

The floor shuddered. "Oooh," we shrieked in unison, and we went from stealing space from each other to hugging each other tight to ensure a peace together as we faced Our Maker.

Ten seconds expanded into ten light years of panic. Finally, the rattling of chairs stopped, the walls and floor normalized, and the slants turned into straight lines again. A realization set in: I had survived major surgery, but Mother Nature could have killed me in one-Kaboom. The school director had suddenly appeared in the hallway, glanced around the wreck of the classroom and asked if we were safe.

"We're okay," the students murmured.

"Anyone hurt?" he asked again, this time directing his gaze to me. When his eyeballs zoomed in on my 42 DDD chest, his mouth fell open.

Silence. A collective shaking of heads. "We are fine, director."

"*Era un temblor, nada más,*" the director said, nothing more than a tremor. His eyes did not blink, frozen into an incredulous stare at my Dolly Parton bust when he asked, "Your students are all here?"

I counted heads. "Yes, all thirty-two."

"Good." He squeezed his eyes shut for a second, shook his head, then turned and disappeared. He probably was wondering what cosmetic surgeon I had used to get such an extraordinary boob job.

I studied my students after he left. "Nothing beats a door frame, right class? Every room has at least one and it's way cheaper than buying an Earthquake Survival Kit."

My students shot me a blank stare. "Don't mind me. I was just trying to be funny, that's all. It was really scary. Wasn't it?"

They nodded solemnly. "*Sí, maestra. Todos estamos bien, gracias a Dios.* Yes, teacher. We're all okay, thank God."

"Let's put the desks and our books in order." The students set out to pick up all the books and backpacks strewn on the floor and we put all the chairs and desks that had been tossed on their sides back upright. "Thanks, everyone, for helping me," I said, regaining my composure.

Once we settled down, a surge of gratitude washed over me. My students had alerted me and protected me. I wanted to hug all of them one by one. We had been close to being pronounced in the past tense ourselves. More eager than ever to teach them, I said, "Repeat after me, "ring, rang, rung."

Later that morning, when leaving the school, I was still trembling. Whew. Two very close calls – first the surgery and then the earthquake, and I was still alive. There weren't any bushes nearby or I would have hugged a bush. I hugged a cement post, as close to a tree as I could get. After looking to the left, then to the right, and finding nobody around, I fell on my knees on a patch of cement, kissed the ground with both arms outstretched, and thanked God by shrieking, "Alive! Alive! Oh my God, I'm alive!"

16

The Bus to the Border

C all me courageous. Call me Amelia Earhart. Call me Sally
Ride if you want, but I did something brave. I traveled
alone, by bus, all the way from the center of Mexico to one of
the northernest borders. Twenty-two hours on a non-stop bus.
This was actually a lot harder than what Amelia and Sally did.
Yes, Amelia crossed the Atlantic Ocean and had to survive
northerly winds and mechanical problems. True that Sally
crossed thousands of miles in space, surviving on dried cereal
cubes and spinach squeezed from a packet. But that's nothing
compared to the hardships I faced. Mine was twenty-two hours
in the same seat, next to Mr. Buzz Saw who used my shoulder
blade as a pillow.

I needed to renew my visa. I chose Juárez even though I
heard Matamoros was much nicer. The city of Juárez lacked a
beach, but rumor was that Juárez had two shopping malls, one
located only steps away from the border, and dozens of
bustling, independent stores. Of course, this was also the
cheapest of the cheapskate's way to renew a visa. Americans
were allowed to stay in Mexico for six months as a tourist.
Then we had to leave Mexico and reenter from the U.S. to stay

for another six months. Which was what I was doing.

As soon as I boarded the bus, it moved at a death-defying speed north. The longer the bus rolled, the stuffier it became, and the grubbier I grew. Grit flew in from the windows, which needed to be kept open or else we would all die of suffocation. I had never minded smells in Mexico. I walked past aromas and odors on the street every day. But now, I couldn't stand the nasty odor at such close quarters, where all the bodies were sweating their chilies off.

One woman in the seat behind me tapped at the window and kept pointing to the wildlife of the desert, "Did you see that?" she'd ask her daughter at her side every few minutes. It must have been her first trip from the capital. She drew my attention to the large nopales, scrawny cows, and jack rabbits. "Oh, look at the roadrunner over there. You see that?"

"Yeah, it's nice," the daughter answered in a monotone.

The bus driver continued moving at nearly the speed of sound. To block out my terror of the road that had turned into a blur, I took several catnaps. Terrible things happened in my vivid disturbing dreams on the bus. I plunged off mountain cliffs, desert snakes slithered up my neck, and I drowned in the Rio Grande. Snores jolted me out of my mini nightmares. The buzz saw noises came from the rotund man sitting next to me, the one with the foul breath resting his head on my shoulder.

At the first brief stop, we all disembarked to grab a bite to eat at a lonely food stand stationed off the highway. My stomach was growling so I ordered a plate of beans and tortillas. I wolfed it down in a few minutes and I sat there and waited for my first signs of indigestion. Luckily, only a few rumbles came. Then we all crammed back on the bus.

In the roughly 1,200 miles between Mexico City and Juárez, there were three checkpoints along the way. At the first one, I was jolted awake by a glaring flashlight of a Customs official. Decked out in his green khaki uniform, he peered down at me. "What do you have in there, Señorita?" he asked, beaming his light on my duffle bag.

"Some books, a blanket and a scarf," I mumbled while

opening my bag for display. "And a bottle of water."

"And in your coat?" the official asked.

I dug my hands into my pockets and showed him. "A toilet paper wad."

The official moved down the bus. He stopped in front of a heavy-set lady. There was no passenger in the seat next to her. She had piled up a variety of hurriedly put together packages. Some looked like clothes, others dishes. She rested her overflowing body on four pillows. I imagined the only way this comfortable set up differed from the one she had at home was her spoiled cat and the television to keep her immobile for a good part of the day. On her head, she wore a red bandana. She didn't appear to be in the least bit ruffled by the custom official's request to go through her parcels. "And what's this?" The official quizzed her as he tore open one of her sloppily taped packages.

"Three sets of dishes, Señor," she said, rather bored by the whole interrogation.

"Do you sell your goods, Señora?" the official asked her.

"Sell?" she answered, "I don't sell anything. These are things I bought for home. They're for my use."

"Your use?" the official asked in a gruff voice. "Three toilet seats for your use?" He tore open another box.

"Yes, one for our house," she said, "and one for my daughter and one for my son."

The official didn't believe her. He made her get off the bus, and she had to unload everything. Package by package, she huffed and puffed while all of us on the bus stared at her climbing up and down the steps over and over. No one offered to lend her a hand. She was on her fifth round of packages and the Customs officials were becoming impatient. "Hurry up! Hurry up now!"

Finally, she was done. "Come with us," they ordered, and led her to a picnic table next to the bus. She was ordered to sit down. We peered through the windows as the officials spread all her clothes out on the table and began picking through them.

Then the bus started up again. We left her there in the middle of the night, in the barren desert. The passenger behind me cleared her throat, leaned over the seat and whispered. "They must have suspected drugs. Her clothes were purposely in disorder."

I disagreed. In my eyes, the swaddled woman was innocent. If she bought a lot of clothing, who was going to fold each piece? Especially not her. Besides, many of the other passengers seemed to be wearing more than one layer of clothing.

Stops for a second and third inspection followed with officials boarding and asking more questions. But there were no incidents like that of the lady left behind. We did, however, stop for brief bathroom breaks.

Eventually, we reached the border city of Juárez. By the time I stumbled off the bus, I had shaky legs and a near-fatal case of a medical condition known technically as "tortilla butt." You would have to know how a señora makes tortillas to truly understand how my gluteus maximus felt. She takes a ball of dough, squeezes it in her two palms, and twenty-two slaps later, has perfectly flattened it out and tosses it onto a Mexican comal or griddle to fry. That was my butt. Flat as that.

The sun was scorching, and my first impression of Juárez was that it was a dusty and blazing hot town. I didn't know where to go but followed my bus buddies to the bridge leading to El Paso. It took me five minutes of limping down a narrow pathway, funneling us into the U.S. customs post. As I entered the border station, I saw the sunburned face of the Texas Customs officer and two cages full of parrots on a long table, all of them silent. "This is the first time I've seen a quiet parrot," I said to the Customs officer, trying to make pleasant small talk, "and not squawking."

"They're drunk," he snorted. "They get the parrots drunk so they're quiet and then stuff 'em with coke."

"On tequila?" I asked.

He ignored my question. "Open your bag. Let's see what you got in there."

I unzipped my duffel. "Nothing." I stretched the sides of my bag so he could see. "Came to buy stuff."

He clawed around my nearly empty bag for two seconds and waved me through.

As soon as I set foot on El Paso soil, I found a post office, went inside and dropped my package to Alex and my family in a slot and voila! In three or four days, they would be at the doorstep of my parents and Alex's house. As I was leaving the post office, an older man approached me and kept pointing to an open letter in his hand and shrugging, palms up. From his gestures, it dawned on me that he didn't know how to read, and was asking for help with his letter. He could tell I was a gringa by my accent but he said nothing as I read his letter to him, nothing but gracias, Señorita, muy amable—very kind. Mexicans are so kind and appreciative. It's like people have their hearts guiding them, their humaneness intact like no other culture.

After an afternoon of shopping, I went back to the checkpoint to enter Mexico, but the border was closed. How could a checkpoint be closed? The border was always supposed to be open. Bursts of laughter came out of the cabin. What were the Custom officials doing in there? I wanted to know. So I snuck up to the cabin, went on tiptoes to peek through the window, and listened. "They're playing cards and drinking beers. I can't believe it!" I whispered. Afraid of getting caught, I hooved it back to the pedestrian line waiting to cross.

17

The News Must Go On

Not long after renewing my visa at the border, I moved from working at *The Observer* to reporting for the Associated Press. Sure enough, just like Ashok had promised, when an opening came up at the international news wire, he had called me and offered me the job. Despite working for my ex-boyfriend, which made it rather interesting, I found my stringer position at the wire service surprisingly yawn producing. I worked mostly in the afternoon and night, and my normal workday consisted of taking Spanish-written wire stories from correspondents stationed in Central and South America, whose stories were really scary—all about bombings and civil wars—and I would translate their turmoil into English.

With each story I filed, I felt a twinge of guilt because I was living a life so far removed from the civil unrest. I was working in a really, really quiet environment. Ha ha! Too quiet. The office didn't have much of a staff, one or two other reporters who mostly worked when I didn't. Ashok was in and out of the office, but mainly out, covering important events and going to important meetings when I was working in the office.

Especially at night, I was mostly flying solo. The only thing that kept me from napping at night was the vibrating hum of the office computers turned on.

Until I heard that *rat-a-tat-tat*.

Rat-a-tat-tat. What was that noise? I looked around the sterile office. It was sparsely furnished and rather hard to hide things. *Rat-a-tat-tat*. That noise again. It wasn't a hissing of a cockroach or a squeaking of a mouse or a buzzing of a fatal mosquito. It was more of a chattering of teeth.

I inspected the legs of my chair, my desk, and my computer station very carefully. Nothing peculiar came scrambling out of the crannies. So the next time I heard the *rat-a-tat-tat*, I simple ignored it. This is what happens when you work too late on a Saturday night all by yourself, Sara. Your imagination runs wild. Paranoia sets in, and the whole place takes on an aura of being infested with roaches like my old Queens apartment.

Rat-a-tat-tat. *Rat-a-tat-tat*.

That was it. I couldn't take it anymore. I stood up and looked around the office for clues. Where was that noise coming from? Somewhere in the back. I went to investigate. There, pushed in a dusty corner, was an old clunky Teletype machine. Could this antique contraption be causing the racket? It was silent at the moment. This device was a long, forgotten relic that went back to a newspaper era when news wires used them for transmitting stories. A retirement road-kill in the age of the Internet.

The Teletype machine suddenly shook frighteningly. *Rat-a-tat*. *Rat-a-tat*. That *was* it.

A Mammoth Manual Typewriter featuring no screen. Giant round keys. Keys named LTRS for letters and FIG for numbers. I named this prehistoric creature Igor because it was so noisy and sounded carnivorous, like it could take a big chunk out of my leg any minute with its keys and—

Rat-a-tat-tat. *Rat-a-tat-tat*. A very large piece of paper kept growing out of its body until it dropped out of the bottom of the machine like a turd. I tore the paper off the machine and read the message.

It said as follows:

"We are holding your reporters hostage."

Bogota bureau, Associated Press

Hostage? Our Associate Press reporters? As in kidnapping and ransom? Shivers ran up my spine. I pictured our reporters, hands tied behind their backs, blindfolded and being dragged into some cold and moldy corner to confess to things they hadn't done. I had to do something quick.

My first impulse was to call Ashok even if he told me not to because he would be out with friends that night. I called him anyway, but he didn't answer. Then I phoned the wire service's headquarters in New York. "Sara, um . . . from the Mexico City Bureau. We got this telex—"

"A telex? From who?" the editor shouted into my ear.

"Rebels in Bogota. They say they've taken our reporters hostage in the AP office there."

"Hostage? Why did they use a Telex?"

"Electricity is out."

"Okay . . . that makes sense since it works on low-wattage like the phone. Go on. Why did they take our reporters hostage?"

"They're demanding," I went on, breathless, "That we run their manifesto on our wire. I got it right here. It's a very long list of demands calling for a more just society. They say they won't release our reporters unless we do."

"We'll deal with their demands later. Message those rebels back immediately. Find out if our reporters are safe. Call me back when you get the answer." The phone went into an unoccupied buzz.

"Right," I muttered and hung up. "Thanks for the help. Ms. New York Editor." What you're saying is that you don't want a needless tragedy and you don't want to deal with it right now."

I went back to Igor and examined the Teletypewriter carefully. Message these guys back? How? How did this prehistoric-creature contraption work? I had a cell phone and a laptop that could do everything but my laundry on weekends, but there I stood, helplessly staring at Igor.

There was only one other person in the building that night. And I went looking for him. He was a Cuban computer technician named Ernesto and he was supposed to be working somewhere in the back in our building. When I found him hidden behind our computer servers, I almost cried for joy "Ernesto! Oh, thank God, you're still here."

"Why? What's the matter?"

I pressed the message into his hands. "Read it."

He scanned it and tapped it hard with his chubby finger. "These rebels, they sound serious."

"What do you think?"

"They mention revolution three times." He looked me straight in the eye. "I know about revolutions. I'm Cuban."

The first time Ernesto mentioned the word *revolution*, I quivered in my Birkenstocks. "You're right," I said after I recovered a bit. "We represent the wrong side of the war, don't we?"

"Yep. The bad guys. The Colombian government is fighting these rebels with the help of *your* government."

"What are we going to do?" I asked. "New York was no help. I called them and they want me to message them back with this Neanderthal machine. It's a Teletypewriter. I have no idea how it works."

"Let's have a look." Ernesto followed me to the office and planted himself in front of Igor. He pushed his oversized horn-rimmed glasses further up his nose and poked around at its keys. "Hmm . . . this thing looks like something that had climbed out of the cave."

"I'm telling you. That's what I thought."

By tips and taps, by clinks and clanks on the keyboard, somehow, Ernesto and I managed to compose a message together in a cryptic prehistoric way. Somewhere, between smoke signals and the Pony Express, we found the magic key SEND and pressed it.

"Are our reporters safe?" the message had said.

I felt the excitement rising in my veins.

"Yes, they are," came the reply back. I breathed out and dialed New York to let them know.

Hours went by, with more agonizing waits and more messages back and forth. Finally, two translated stories later and 63 times circling around the office, the rebels' list of demands ran on the wire and the rebels released our reporters unharmed.

I pushed Igor back into the far corner of the office, where it could quietly go back to gathering dust in the corner. I turned to Ernesto and beamed. "We did it!"

He chuckled and blew out a gust of relief. "Yeah, well, it's three o'clock in the morning."

"I love it! This was the most excitement I've had since breaking up with my ex-boyfriend José."

Ernesto scratched his bald head. "Well, that was enough action for tonight and for the whole month, if you ask me."

"Geez, you're a lifesaver. I'm sorry I can't offer you a Cuban cigar."

"No problem. You know all Cubans love baseball."

"Okay, I'll buy you a baseball then, but if I can't find one, would a pepperoni pizza be okay?"

"Sounds good, *yuma*." *Yuma* is a nickname that Cubans give Americans.

The next morning, I called my mother to tell her about the terrifying night before, how I managed a crisis situation with rebels in Colombia. And I told her how much I loved her.

"This is a sign, Sara. You should think about that," my mother said from faraway Michigan.

"A sign of what, Mom?"

"You're good at crisis management. You could be making money as a 911 operator or a dispatching police officer. You know, sending cops to crime scenes."

"What are you talking about, Mom? I like what I am doing."

"Just what I said." I had forgotten my mother's voice had built-in speakers attached to it. "It would pay better than writing for free in Mexico."

"That's crazy! Mom, I can't believe you said that! I love

writing and reporting. I love what I do. You don't get it. Mom, I have to go."

"Just a minute. Not so fast. Mark Goldstein asked about you again."

I knew it. I knew she would bring up Mark Goldstein. I knew exactly what she would say next. *If the wedding bells were ever to ring in St. Bridget's Church in Detroit, I had to get busy.* "I don't care an iota about Mark Goldstein. Forget about him, Mom, okay? Can't you understand that?"

"Well, I was just relaying the message from Mark, that's all. You don't have to bite off my neck."

My mother couldn't help it. She had never read anything by Gloria Steinman. She had no clue that I'd just won the Silver Medal in the Journalist Olympics. I ended the conversation with my best If-I-Don't-Go-Now-I'm-Going-To-Explode.

18

Stairway to the Underworld

After Ashok learned of my heroics solving the rebel crisis, he urged me to take a few days off. "Go see Palenque," he suggested. "You'll see the most beautiful Mayan ruins, and you'll be in nature."

"Nature? Who says I like nature?" For a woman like me, who stayed glued to the city, going to remote ruins conjured up pictures of ordinary people like me turning into howling coyotes when the moon came out.

"You'd like it," Ashok said.

I shook my head. "Nah, I don't think so." I needed a metropolis to feel at home.

Ashok went on convincingly, "Seriously, Sara, you should just go. It would clear your head and you'd relax. The Palenque ruins are the jewels of the Americas. They date back to the seventh century. It'll be amazing!"

"Let me think about it," I said, trying not to focus too much on my city complex.

"If you want, I'll come with you."

"Thanks for the offer, but I don't think that would really be a good idea." At that point, I just wanted to get as far away as possible from the world of "urgent" or "deadline" and with no male complications. But Ashok was right. I needed to clear my head and relax. But I'd lose income by taking days off work so I thought of my former boss Guido. I called him and convinced him that I would do a touristy travel feature on the archaeological ruins for *The Observer*. Little did I know that to make a trip to Palenque, I had to fly into Villahermosa and from there, take a van to the ruins.

So there I was in the jungle of Chiapas, bouncing along a potholed road on my way to this archeological wonder. I told myself I would first go inside the famous King Pakal's tomb and get my writing duties over with as fast as I could. Then I would kick back eating mangos and papayas in my hotel. After all, the primary goal was to relax. So far, I hadn't seen any signs of human habitation on this remote road winding through the rain forest. I was taking in a lot of greenery though. If I had wanted this much greenery, I would have ordered a salad and skipped the trip. Driving through the jungle, I must confess, the smoggy capital began to look real good to me, like my natural habit, in fact, and this strange humanless environment was making me feel a million miles away from relaxed.

Thirty seconds after I thought that, came a blood-curdling roar.

"Did you hear that?" I whispered.

The driver let out a low chuckle.

Then right before my very eyes, a very long tail from an unidentified member of the animal kingdom vaulted past our van swinging and dashing through the vegetation, moving from treetop to treetop in a blur.

I gulped.

"Howler monkeys. Don't worry. I have a machete in the back."

Machete? I broke out in a torrent of sweat.

"A monkey is four times stronger than a man, so you have to be careful," the van driver said matter-of-factly.

"Right," I remarked, and tugged at my white linen shirt clinging to my chest. It was soaked. It will be a miracle if I get out of here alive, I thought.

"Relax," the van driver chuckled. "You're on a major road."

Relax? Did he say relax? How could anyone relax? How I got into this predicament, on this remote ribbon of pavement, was kind of spur of the moment in the first place. Did the driver even know that my love for nature was limited to a Sunday stroll through Chapultepec Park? That I had failed to get a single tropical disease shot before this trip? That I was completely untrained at swatting fatal mosquitoes?

Then a bird screeched. Not an ordinary street pigeon cooing a bit about the scenery. That I'd recognize in a second, but the most ear-wrenching screech that went on for about five hundred minutes. Like some male bird arguing with his wife over infidelity somewhere in Guatemala via air waves. My ears throbbed so much I took my palms and folded my ear lobes back like a flap of an envelope until the screeching stopped.

"Scarlet macaws," the driver announced.

What else was lurking behind the vines or the tangle of trees? Let's see, howling monkeys . . . shrieking birds, deadly scorpions, and venomous snakes? And what about the fatal mosquitos? I'll bet they were the size of aircraft carriers.

"Enjoy the fresh air," the driver said.

He had to be kidding, wasn't he? It was stiflingly, tropically humid. At this point, I was starting to get a bad feeling about all this. Ashok should have come with me. I was ready to take a cab back to civilization. I needed to tell the driver to let me out here, but I was afraid.

Instead, I peered out the window to spot a man lying on a hammock strung between two trees. He wore a long white gown, had a pitch-black long hair that framed his chiseled face. Razor straight bangs ran across his forehead. As the van rumbled by him, his piercing eyes bore a hole in me.

I leaned close to the driver and shouted over the rattles of the van. "That guy on his hammock, did you see him? Does he belong to some tribe?"

The driver threw back his head in a chuckle. "We just passed a Lacandón Maya."

"A Mayan?"

"That's right."

"They're not all dead?"

"Oh, no. Mayans are very much alive in southern Mexico," the driver said. "And in Central America."

"A modern Mayan? Really? I mean, how did they survive the Spanish? I thought they had been all killed off."

"The jungle. The jungle saved them. The Spanish couldn't get to them."

"Oh, and they didn't all die off from disease?"

"Not if the Spanish didn't get to them."

"Amazing. Why don't the history books say that?"

"Don't worry, you're not the only one who thinks they're all dead," the driver said. "Yesterday or today, Mayans are Mayans."

"Are there many left?"

"Millions. Six million live in Mexico, Guatemala, Belize. Speak different Mayan languages too."

Millions? Did he say millions? Millions of modern Mayans. As my head thumped against the roof of the van, I thought about this. I just got a glimpse of a real Mayan, a descendant of an indigenous society that gave the world the 365-day solar calendar and the concept of zero. A living, breathing Mayan. All of a sudden, the scary sounds of the jungle faded a teensy bit into the leafy background as I felt a surge of excitement about the trip for the first time.

We arrived at the ruins. I stepped into a little museum housing a government official who I assumed was the caretaker. "Buenos días, oficial," I said in a voice weakened by my animal experiences in the van.

"You have a letter and identification?" inquired the official in a brisk tone.

I did. I pulled out my papers from my backpack and handed the press letter that gave special permission to go inside the tomb. I steadied myself against the counter to brace myself for the caretaker's verdict. King Pakal's tomb was normally closed to the general public, off limits to all but serious Mayan researchers. Even with a press letter, permissions often depended on the whim of various authorities in Mexico. Especially since the tomb was the Americas' equivalent of the King Tut's tomb in Egypt. "As you can see, I'm writing a feature for *The Observer*," I pointed to my name on the letter.

"Hmm . . ." He paused every now and then to eyeball me and then went back to reading the letter.

Then, just so there were absolutely no doubts as to if I were a professional journalist, I dug out my press credential from the Associated Press and showed it to him. "I also have an international press credential."

"Hmm . . ." He continued reading without looking up.

Standing there waiting, I blurted "trámites" out loud. This means red tape. I was sure the caretaker heard this, so I was half expecting for him to take his sweet old time inspecting my letter, and maybe even worse, refuse to sign and stamp it. But to my surprise, a few minutes later, he handed it back and waved me away. I padded out to the central plaza of the ruins. and headed toward the main pyramid where the seventh century King Pakal was buried.

It was called the Temple of the Inscriptions. When I drew near and got a good look at the steep stairway leading up to the temple, I suddenly understood what the tourist authorities had told me about Palenque. They had said it was a historic site suited for those who physically run on the hardy side, emphasizing rugged backpackers, mainly European. One glimpse of these steps was all I needed to realize that they were absolutely positively right. This was a dumb place to go to relax. This wasn't for me, whose most strenuous activities were finger push-ups on a keyboard.

A few feet away was a Dutch family standing around with their eyes zeroed in on the steps to the pyramid. The woman in the group was leafing through a Dutch guidebook on Mexico. The man was taking pictures of the steps. The young boy was squinting at the pyramid, using his palm over his eyes for an awning. Apparently, they weren't going up the steps of the pyramid. Just taking pictures and studying its majestic beauty. But I had two thousand words to write by Thursday so I was sticking with it. I had come all this way to see the tomb of the great Mayan ruler, and was getting paid for it, so no matter how infernally hot the day was, I was going up those steps.

"You going up in this heat?" one of the Dutch tourists gave me a sideways glance and asked in an English far more perfect than mine. He studied me slipping my arms through the shoulder straps of my backpack.

I nodded. "I am."

"We'll go up once it cools down," he added.

"Well, here goes," I said, and turned to face the giant highway to heaven. I began my climb up and up and up. Nearly one hundred feet in the sky.

By the time I reached the top of the pyramid, I was looking for an oxygen mask. The Dutch tourists were enjoying the view of the dumb American tourist from their view below. The boy was pointing at me, the woman was frantically waving at me, and the man was still taking pictures. I suspected they were remarking, "Look at her! What a dope going all the way up there in this inferno, and knowing there is no water at the top. She knows nobody can get inside the tomb."

I waved back, dripping with sweat, and shouted. "See? Still alive! By the way, up here is a sweeping panoramic view and you're missing the whole thing." I was sure they couldn't hear me and it felt good to shout out. Catching my breath, I turned around to face the magnificent Mayan figures carved in stone that graced the entrances of the roofed temple. Glyphs. I had no idea what the writing said, but I communicated with the Mayan scribe at the moment.

"What was your water situation way back when?" I asked the glyphs. "Is that what this writing is about? Because I'm pretty thirsty at this point."

With work to do, I dug out my notebook and tourist brochures and wrote a vivid description of the glyphs and the climb of what seemed like a thousand steps for my article. Technically, I noted, the pyramid rose 85 feet in the air, according to the educational literature, but I simply put "way too many" steps. What's more, I thought readers would be able to understand how steep the pyramid was if I described its height by saying that it just went up and up to about a quarter of the way to God, and then just stopped. At the top was Mayan script about the lives of the rich and famous. The best part was still to come. I was going inside the temple to see the cave-like tomb of the Mayan King Pakal.

I put away my notebook, stuck my head inside and eyed the hole of the temple. A dark, dank, stinky hole. Maybe bats caused the stink. I remembered reading somewhere that bats roosted inside old temples. I sure hoped I wouldn't encounter any of those hairy rats with wings. Anyway, it was a deep hole, so deep it looked like a silver or gold mine—maybe 10,000 feet deep (just guessing) with a set of narrow stairs barely lit by a string of light bulbs. Oh, but at the bottom, I reminded myself, was King Pakal's tomb with the famous sarcophagus lid.

Personally, if anyone would have told me that I needed a male bodyguard to go inside this temple before this trip, I would have sent them to the moon on a one-way ticket. But now, yes now—seeing how deep and narrow the steps were that led down to the tomb, with a very real possibility of never coming up—that was when I wanted Ashok to be at my side. At this point, I'd have even taken crotch-grabbing José for some protection.

"Well, is it going to be today or next Monday?" I asked myself. With one fleeting moment of courage, I pushed off to grab a foothold on the first stair. My left foot slipped off and I scrambled to keep my balance. Wow, these steps were as slimy as a wet bar of soap, I thought. I would have to back down the steps on all fours, slipping and sliding, real cat-like.

"Step, one more step, that's it, one more, Sara," I said aloud to keep my courage up, reminding myself that I had wanted to do this. Remember? This was a once-in-a-reporter-lifetime adventure. Remember? I chanted, Mexico was not for the meek and mild. Mexico was not for the meek and mild. Down, down I went, step by step. It was creepy. Creepy as in The

Mummy movie but instead of descending into an Egyptian tomb, Sara was descending into a Mayan one. In the movie, beetles attack the explorers and crawl under their skin and eat them alive. A mummified priest becomes mortal again and exacts revenge on the living. "Stop the drama, Sara," I told myself. At one point, when I thought I sensed a bat flapping its wings overhead, I pushed on, telling myself, "You're halfway there," and continuing my pep talk, "Besides, bats eat insects. You are not an insect Sara."

Down I went. There was even a U-turn to the stairs, I followed the turn, trusting that King Pakal's tomb was down there somewhere. As long as the Mayan king didn't come back to life, or I wouldn't have to drink a potion called the "Blood of Pakal" once I got down there, or be sacrificed to the Corn God and served up on a slab of stone, I was willing to keep going. Down the slimy steps I went until I reached the bottom.

The ground. I exhaled. Long and deep. I made it. I tugged at the medal I wore around my neck, rubbed my fingers over the Virgin engraving and kissed Her. "Thank you for being my bodyguard, Virgencita."

Now, to see the King. I peeked through thick metal bars that were protecting the famous tomb. There it was. Yes. The famous stone lid over Pakal's tomb. It was carved with a faded image of a Tree of the World with a Celestial Bird perched on it. Supposedly, the tree and the bird were symbols of the kingdom of heaven. I studied the image of King Pakal carved on the lid. The king was emerging from the Underworld, which was exactly what I was about to do. Go up.

Time to go up, up, up Sara. The tomb was lovely and all, but at that moment, I was ready because of that noise—unsure if my own heart was thumping away or if a bat was flying around. I certainly felt a panic attack coming on. I tried to calm my panic with the voice of reason again. "You are a Giant Female and not an insect. But another tiny voice of hysteria squeaked back. "What if the bat swoops down for the Giant Female Mosquito in a rare case of mistaken identity?"

Just when I calmed myself down enough to lift both hands

and feet onto the first steps to climb the narrow stairs up, a bat came swooping down and one of its leathery wings brushed against my hair.

I let out a curdling scream. "Off me! Off me! Get it off me! You freaking flying radar rat!"

The bat was climbing, diving, banking and doing acrobatics in a circle around my face.

Like a wild woman, I waved my arms in the air. "Get out of my hair! Get out of my hair! A bat! Help! A bat! Someone help! I'm being attacked by a bat!"

No one appeared at the mouth of the cave.

Up the stairs I went, crawling up much faster than I had climbed down. A cheetah sprint. Till I made it outside.

Once in the fresh air, I sprinted down the outside steps of the pyramid to ground level, real cheetah-like, too. I looked around once my feet touched ground. The Dutch tourists were gone. I looked down at my pants. They were covered with a moss-like slimy substance.

That night, I collapsed from exhaustion on a soft bed in a tiny cabin with a thatched roof and mosquito screen all around it. Lots of tropical fresh air breezing through despite the fact that I reeked of insect repellent just to be on the safe side. After my descent into the cave-like underworld, it felt like I was sleeping in The Garden of Eden. Most importantly, I did it all by myself, without the help of Ashok or José. I must confess, though, I think I survived with a little help from the virgencita, who kept me safe.

When Ashok later asked me how Palenque was, I told him outside of the fact that I nearly got inhaled by a bat, I really enjoyed seeing the ruins and King Pakal's tomb.

"Wasn't it relaxing?"

"Relaxing? No, I wouldn't call it that

19

Stubbing Your Toe on History

Y ou can't walk a single block in this city without stubbing
your toe on History.

    I pass a bakery and spot an Aztec calendar hanging
on the wall of the shop. It displays an image of a five-hundred-
year-old Aztec prince holding a dying woman in his arms.
History.

    Whenever I encounter a person or a street named after a
Famous Indigenous, you know, a name with too many X's or
C's or U's, like Cuauhtémoc (kwou-TAY-mahk),
Cuitláhuac(kwit-LA-wahk), Xiuhcoatl (ZAYA-ka-whatl), it's as
if the person or street were introducing themselves to me, "Hi,
I'm History."

    Indigenous tribes are really good at thinking up hard-to-say
and hard-to-spell names with the letter X. It can sound like an
"s" or "sh," or "j" or even "k," and your guess is as good as
mine.

    If I try to pronounce the name of this sort, my tongue
tangles in my throat like I'm choking on a chicken bone. A
purplish tint washes over my face in an attempt to let the name
out but it never gets even close to the tip of my tongue.

Coming out of the Metro, I ran into History again. I passed an Indian beggar crouching on a blanket. She outstretched her arm and curled her withered fingers into a cup. "*Una limosna, Señorita, por el amor de Dios?* A little charity, for the love of God?"

The lump in my throat grew into the size of a boulder. How come Indians were begging on the streets when Mexicans seemed so proud of their indigenous history? On one hand, I had seen their hallowed Aztec stone calendar and artifacts of the Mayan ruins displayed at the National Anthropology Museum. On the other hand, my eavesdropping on stressed-out Mexican moms revealed mothers scolding their children by saying, "Don't act Indian." What was going on with Mexican identity? I wanted to find out.

I thought my tutor Francisco would have a clue. At my next Spanish lesson, I brought up the love/hate relationship with the Indians that I observed. "It's a paradox, it really is, the whole Mexican identity."

Francisco just listened intently but never said a word. He returned to correcting my trill of the Spanish "r" so I could say "rico" (delicious or rich) properly. Instead of the "r" in the roar of an engine, it sounded like he wanted me to flutter the "r" like the wings of a butterfly.

"You sound as if you're choking on a butterfly," he said.

"My 'r' really sounds like that?"

"Yeah. It's terrible."

"Don't be mean. I'm trying."

"Forget about trying. Let your tongue roll." He tilted his head back and demonstrated. "Like this."

"That's a flutter if you ask me, not a roll."

After ten minutes, Francisco suddenly asked, "Have you heard of Malinche?"

"You mean Cortés' interpreter? The one who helped Cortés beat the Aztecs?"

"She was *more* than his interpreter. She was his mistress. She gave him a son, Martín."

"Really? Wow, Mexican soap operas go back a long way."

"Yes," Francisco said softly as we sipped our coffee,

"Martín is considered the first Mexican born of mixed blood, the first mestizo."

"I *knew* Malinche was important."

"Cortés wrote about how important she was in his letters. He said, 'After God we owe this conquest of New Spain to Doña Marina.'"

"I suppose Mexicans will never forgive her for that."

"Never. Many of us think of her as a traitor. That's why when a Mexican talks bad about Mexico or acts "too foreign," we'll call him a *malinchista*."

"You're not considered a *malinchista* for tutoring a gringa, are you?"

"Of course not!" he said, his face flushing.

Was he telling me all this to appeal to my love of history? This must be an act of wooing, of the intellectual kind. An idea popped into my head. "Hey, Francisco," I leaned toward him, "you want to help me with something?"

"I'm already helping you with something. Your Spanish."

"Something *else*."

"What?"

I edged closer to him until my nose was an inch from his nose. Sharing something very clandestine had to be shared at a proper distance.

His eyes glimmered, his ears twitched, and he whispered, "What do you need help with? Tell me. Anything."

"Would you help me find out where Cortés and Malinche are buried? See if there are any statues or monuments of them in the city? I haven't seen any, *have you*? Wouldn't that be something to find?" My face lit up with excitement.

A flash of anger danced across his face. "What are you talking about? You crazy? You want me to help you find a 500-year-old ticking bomb of history?"

"C'mon. It would be fun."

"No!" He stood up, walked to the kitchen door and looked out.

I had made him mad. I didn't want to get him mad. I tried again, this time, in a softer and whispering tone, "C'mon."

He spun around and held his finger to his temple. His words were shooting out at 106 words a minute. "I know what you are thinking. You're thinking I'm going to help you. You're wrong. Do you know why? I'll tell you why. You haven't seen any Cortés or Malinche statue and I haven't seen any Cortés or Malinche statue because there aren't any. Get it?"

"We don't know that for sure."

"I'm sure."

"C'mon. Please?" I turned on the pineapple sauce. "What happened to your I'll-help-you-with-anything attitude?"

He shook his head in disgust. "Give me a good reason to."

"Think of it as a mission. Whatever we find, whether it's a tomb, a sculpture, a monument, would show me how Mexicans think of their Spanish and Indian blood and how they want to remember or forget their past."

"Let me get this straight. You want to track down the tombs and sculptures of the conquistador Cortés and his mistress Malinche for an abstract reason like identity? Am I missing something?"

"Yeah. That's what I want to do. That's it."

Francisco put his palm on his chest. "I can tell you how I feel. I'm mestizo. One hundred percent. Is that good enough for you?"

I gave him my laser beam stare. "No."

He shook his head. "It's wacky. This idea of yours."

"It is?"

"Yes, but I will accompany you on your silly mission."

I jumped out of my chair and planted a kiss on his cheek.

"You, gringuita, are very persuasive."

"Oh, you're the best, Francisco. Just think, you will be aiding and abetting me in my covert operation on Mexican identity."

Francisco turned his head. "Don't I get a kiss on the other cheek, too?"

A week later, Francisco was complaining about what he got himself into. He said searching for a Cortés or Malinche statue in a city of twenty million people would be like looking for a contact lens at the bottom of the sea. He called it the Mission Improbable. "So you'd better do your research beforehand." By the sound of his voice, I knew he really meant it too.

For my Mission Improbable, I rooted around the Internet and failed to find a record of how or when Malinche died, let alone where she was buried. As for Cortés, things got really complicated after he died in Spain in 1547, at age 62. Just like Malena had told me, Cortés only got to take naps in the afterlife and there was no resting in peace at all.

First, Cortés was buried in Seville, Spain. Then he was roused to go on an epic journey crossing the Spanish desert, turbulent Atlantic seas, and the rugged mountains of the Sierra Madre, even weathering Mexico's War of Independence before he was finally buried inside the wall of a church. After being buried in several places around Mexico and dug up again by who knows who, I had the feeling that we were not dealing with the local funeral parlor either.

Where was this church? *In Mexico City.* When I found that out, I phoned Francisco and shouted in his ear. "He's right here! In Mexico City! Buried in some church!"

Forty-five minutes later, the two of us were standing inside that church, in front of Cortés' coat of arms that marked his tomb on the wall. Victory number one. I had found Cortés' tomb.

I was so excited I was about to explode. My mind raced ahead. I wanted to know where a Cortés sculpture was next. Was it close by?

I turned to Francisco. "Let's go to the hospital next door. It carries the same name as the church. Maybe they have something there."

It turned out the hospital was founded by Cortés in 1524 and in its interior courtyard, at the bottom of a beautiful staircase, was a bust of Cortés.

"See, Francisco? I told you so." I pulled at his arm for him to take a closer look.

"Stop squeezing my arm."

I let go, but rubbed it in. "And Cortes is displayed *in public*."

Francisco shrugged. "Okay, he founded the hospital, that's why. And I wouldn't say that it's exactly *publicly* displayed inside a courtyard of a hospital. To me, it's more like *hidden*."

"*Still.*"

A Cortés statue. Victory Two. Feeling invincible by these finds, we searched the hospital grounds for a statue of Malinche. We didn't find one, but there was a mural painted on the wall that showed the first meeting between Cortés and Montezuma. Sure enough, Malinche was at Cortés' side as the interpreter.

Full of confidence and a sense of adventure, I thought I'd gamble and ask Francisco if he could sacrifice the rest of his afternoon and go to Coyoacán with me next.

"Now what?" Francisco was asking. "What's in Coyoacán?"

"A mestizo monument. Supposedly, it's located in a hidden park somewhere. There's supposed to be a statue of Cortés, Malinche and their son, Martín."

"You're really into this, aren't you? One Cortés tomb and one statue of him aren't enough?"

I shook my head. "You never know. We might be on a winning streak."

He reluctantly agreed and we took the Metro to Coyoacán. We had to ask a policeman where the tiny park called Xicoténcatl was. We walked some more and had to ask another policeman and still another policeman until five policemen later, we finally found ourselves in front of an unmarked door of the park. We went inside and poked around the trees until we caught sight of a life-size bronze sculpture of La Malinche sitting down with a standing Cortés at her side.

"See? There it is! History!"

"*¡Eso es!* That's it!" Francisco said. He approached the statue and read *The Monument of the Mixed Race. The Mestizo Monument.* "Well, what do you know. You found it."

I snapped away taking pictures of it. "Wait a minute. Where is the statue of Martín, their illegitimate son you told me about? That was supposed to be part of the sculpture, according to the article I read.

"You can't believe everything you read on the Internet."

"No, it should be here. It's missing. I bet someone took it."

I sat on a bench across from the monument to think. It was really an amazing sight. Francisco sat next to me, his arm slipping ever so slyly over my back at first and then resting loosely over my shoulder. I decided not to make a fuss about it since I was busy thinking about my findings.

One thing seemed clear. Malinche was a one-woman argument for how women can change the course of history. Yet she remained the patron saint of women scorned. She had been discarded even though she played such a pivotal role in Mexican history as Cortés' companion and mistress; both after she helped Cortés achieve his conquest goals and after she had given birth to his son. Her story reminded me of my own.

How I had helped Marcelo with his English and helped him understand American culture since he had come from Mexico and had been in the States for a few months when I had met him. I was Marcelo's mistress without actually knowing I was. And I'll never know how long I had been "the other woman." I felt discarded at the hospital entrance the day I met the wife and they dropped me off at the train station on that rainy Christmas Day without saying a word. Useful until dumped, an old story for me, for Malinche, and even for Frida.

"Hey," Francisco removed his arm around my shoulder and pointed to his watch. "It's getting late, we should go."

I only half heard. "What?"

"The sun's going down. You're lost in your own world."

I stood up. "You're right."

"Trust me. I've digested more than my minimum daily requirement of History," Francisco said, but there was a glint in his eyes that I had never seen before.

As we walked back through the streets of Coyoacán, I told Francisco that I'd have to walk a mile or more in huaraches to understand how Mexicans considered themselves mestizo, but in their core, identified with the Indian.

"So you got answers to your identity questions?"

"Kind of. I know nobody wants to even think about Cortés.

He's a villain. I think when he died, he was treated kind of like a war criminal. Everybody wanting him but not really wanting him because it might cause trouble for the countries if they take him."

"Told you. The five-hundred-year-old ticking time bomb that I was talking about it."

"You were right. He's the evil genie stuffed inside a glass case inside an old church and next to it, if you look real hard, you'll come across his bust."

"Besides that," Francisco said, "he's hidden away with his mistress inside a very difficult-to-find park along with his illegitimate son, who appears to be missing."

"The soap opera continues."

Francisco let out a chuckle. "So we're done with our silly mission?"

My head bobbed up and down. I was proud of our mission accomplished. Even if Francisco said it was a silly mission, he seemed to enjoy being a part of it. My published stories might never get awards, let alone a Pulitzer, but my investigative skills, that might be something to brag about.

20

The Boob Tube

I had the flu, and even worse, a bad fever that made me hallucinate and see my mother everywhere . . . I wanted a greasy chicken soup with noodles in it . . . and giant egg noodles were dancing in the living room . . .I was carrying on a conversation with the Virgin of Sorrows, the painting hanging on the wall.

Just when I saw no ray of hope, a spark flickered in my low-functioning brain. I'd watch Mexican television. I searched for a remote control to turn on the TV none in sight. So with all my strength I could muster, I crawled over to the TV set and pressed *click*.

The blue screen lit up to a soap opera *Without Breasts There Is No Paradise*. A teenage girl named Catalina wanted larger breasts as a solution to her family's economic woes. I couldn't relate. I had breasts the size of regulation baseballs but never wanted larger ones. Two weeks of Dolly Parton breasts when recovering from breast surgery was enough. They hurt and they were heavy.

The TV actress named Catalina also suffered all sorts of romantic problems with the boy she really loved. *That* part I could relate to. I lay there watching the Mexican mush while tearing into a box of Ritz crackers and covering the couch with crumbs. "Ugh!" I punched my pillow and in my state of delirium, started talking to it. "Enough about *you*. Right pillow? What about *me*? I had my own soap opera with Marcelo. I had blocked out the details but the general plot was still there. I asked the soapbox, "You want to hear mine?"

The TV set gave no answer back, so I threw the blanket over my head to take a nap but a knock at the door jolted me awake. Stumbling to the door, I swung it open about six inches to find Malena standing there and looking me squarely in the eyes.

"Well, there you are, in flesh and blood!" she said in her smoky voice.

"Malena? How did you get here? I mean, past the front gate?"

"Being sick is wonderful, isn't it, sweetie?" she rasped and stepped inside my apartment.

"You interrupted my pity party."

"I hadn't heard from you for a couple of days so I called your work, and Ashok told me you had been out for three days sick. I thought I'd pay you a little visit."

"Aw . . . look at me!" My palm swept over my blanket-red-polka-dot- pajama combo and stringy hair. "I look awful!"

"Awful is relative. You look like you don't feel well, that's all."

I shuffled back to the sofa and collapsed. "You shouldn't be here. I've got the flu and I'll give it to you."

"Nonsense. Three days and you're likely no longer contagious. Look what I've brought!" Malena pulled out a box of tea from her bag and swung it in the air. "Chamomile tea." I waved it away. "Not for me."

"Chamomile tea, my dear, was my granny's solution to all things."

"I *hate* that stuff. Smells like hay. Sorry."

"Okay, suit yourself." Malena disappeared into the kitchen and came back sipping a steaming cup of the hay tea. Her eyes landed on the television. "What are you watching?"

"Some terrible soap opera."

"*Chica*, don't you know Mexican TV is hazardous to your health?"

"You're too late to warn me. I'm already sick."

"A horrible, horrible show. Look!" I pointed to the soap opera on breasts.

"Let's change this," Malena said.

It landed on a clown program.

"Not that," we said in unison.

A game show called *Singing for a Dream*?

"Just about anything on the *tele* can be fatal," Malena said. "Let's give it a chance."

Singing for a Dream was an amateur singer show like *American Idol* except it was different. The Mexican contestants explained why they were on the show, to win prize money. They broke down in tears in front of the camera as they shared their very sad stories ranging from being blind to being paralyzed. A man described how he was a father of seven and ended up declaring bankruptcy and another lady was singing for an organ transplant.

"Wow, this is depressing," I said, turning to Malena. "So many sad stories. I can't watch it anymore." I just lay there stunned for a minute. I should toss the TV right out the window. I guess having the flu wasn't so bad, after all. I mean, compared to bankruptcy, paralysis and blindness.

Malena agreed. "Very depressing, *chica*. We watch three shows in a row like these and I'm sure we would be declared legally dead."

"I do have hardships, Malena," I said. "I've been in a semi-coma on this couch for three days."

"I know."

"I do have woes." A tiny spider was slowing crawling up my pajamas from the couch leg and I crushed it and brushed the dead spider from my pajamas.

"Since we're talking about hardships, darling," Malena said, surveying my living room with her eyes resting on the seven swords piercing the heart of the Virgin of Sorrows. "Weren't you looking for another place to live? I just heard about a vacant room to rent. One of my inside contacts, of course. Are you interested?"

"You know I've been looking. Where is it?"

"It's in a big old house where you share with others, but they rent out individual rooms. It's in Polanco."

"Polanco?" The neighborhood of Polanco was a leafy suburb. "Are you kidding me because I'm in no mood for jokes, Malena—"

"Quite serious." She took another look around the room. "I believe it would be better than here. More modern. My guess is that there won't be any 'can't-flush-the-toilet-paper issues,' at least, I don't think there would be."

"Wait a minute. You're talking about a place where I can magically flush away the paper again?"

"I'd imagine so."

Thinking about a new apartment, with new piping where you can flush away the toilet paper, was hard to believe

"No more throwing the soiled paper in a basket next to the toilet?"

"I can't imagine that being the case."

"But you don't know for sure?"

"I already told you that I believe the Polanco house is fairly new."

"Did I tell you about the time I was caught off guard?" I asked.

"Is it about toilets?"

I nodded. "I just wanted to tell you about this time."

"Okay. Go ahead."

"Well, it was a while ago, I was still with José. We were in a hurry to go out to eat. I was rushing around and changing my clothes so fast that I forgot to transfer my toilet paper wad to the new pocket. You know those folded neat squares of toilet paper origami that I stash away in my pocket and carry around wherever I go?

"Is there a point to the story?" Malena asked.

"Yeah, I'm getting to it. So after the meal, I went to the bathroom in the restaurant, you know, how in those fancy restaurants, there's a lady, whose sole function, as far as I can tell, is to dish out two squares of toilet paper on your way to the stall."

"That's her job," Malena added.

"I know it is, but before I could snatch two squares out of her fingers, I had to give her a *propina*, a tip. You know, the social grease here."

"So? I don't get your point, Sara."

"I'm getting to it. So I was stingy on the *propina*, and sure enough, I was forced to call the paper-rationing lady by wriggling my hand under the stall time until she found me. Over here, over here, *oiga, Señora, para acá*, I shouted. She finally came and I practically clinged to her legs negotiating under the stall for another fold or two."

"That's your story?" Malena asked.

"Yeah, that's it. It was so humiliating. One thing about the whole shortage-of-toilet-paper issue here. You'll never come out of the restroom dragging a piece of toilet paper out of the back of your skirt."

"Getting back to this apartment," Malena said. "It might be worth checking out."

"Yeah, I want to. Do you think it'll be quiet, too?"

"I'd think so, it is a nicer area than these prehistoric parts where—"

I didn't let Malena finish telling me about it. I jumped off the sofa and gave her a big hug. "You're a darling and I'd kiss you but I don't want you to get sick."

"You'll be happier there, I think."

Geez, Malena was in a motherly mode. So rare.

"Well, it's getting . . . zzzzzzzzzz" Malena said. Her voice died away in sort of a mashed potato mumble.

"What did you say?" I mumbled to Malena, and heard the door shut.

The Mexican National Anthem woke me. The roaring cannons in the anthem signaled the end of television programming for the day. I managed to extract myself from the couch to click the TV off, move to the bed and return to my half sleep, with random streams of thought about the evening . . . Malena is one of the best things about living in Mexico . . . she is a real friend to come by to visit me and cheer me up the old-fashioned way. She had even given me a tip on a new place to live. Wouldn't that be something if I got into a nicer place?

21

A Room on the Roof

A week later, the manager of the house in Polanco phoned me with an offer to show me the vacant room to rent. That is, if I was still interested.

"Still interested?" I wanted to shout. *Are Mariachis Mexican? Are chiles the National Vegetables? Is soccer The State Religion?* But I knew it would be rude so I contained my excitement and politely told him, "Yes, I'm still *very* interested," and promised to meet him in a half hour.

"Good. I'll be waiting for you," the manager said.

I hung up and waved my red dish towel through the air and jumped off the floor a couple of feet. *¡Olé!* If everything went right, I could move in later that day. *¡Olé!* That meant I'd no longer have to tip toe on ice-cold floors to light a match under the water tank. *¡Olé!* The suburbs? Oh, I could see it all. Magic toilets, hot showers, and noisy sprinklers making circles on freshly mowed lawns. *¡Olé!* Polanco Paradise, here I come. Wait a minute. I glanced at my watch. My paradise would be gone if I didn't get a move on it. With twenty minutes to spare, there would be no messing around with the Metro. I'd flag down a taxi.

Cruising the tree-lined streets of Polanco, I fell immediately in love with the neighborhood. Such a lovely, lovely, quiet neighborhood. I passed streets named after writers such as Newton, Socrates and Edgar Allen Poe. Imagine this rookie journalist clutching a lovely address for a house on Emerson, in honor of Ralph Waldo Emerson, one of my favorite writers. Oh, what a premium residential upgrade. As for a room, I wasn't asking too much. A place with no *ranchera* music blaring, no Drunk Husband visits, and if the toilet flushed paper magically away, all the better.

When my taxi deposited me in front of a house painted bright orange and wedged between two older apartment buildings, I was thrilled. Okay, the manicured lawn and noisy sprinklers making circles on the lawn were missing, *but still*. I pressed the buzzer intercom and Alfonso, the manager, met me at the gate. On a tour of the house, he first led me to the kitchen on the ground floor. I was extremely alert to every detail. "Somewhere in the house lives a real food thief," he warned. "We still don't know who it is so be careful what food you leave."

"Okay, no problem," I said. I was more worried about the hot water. "On the phone you mentioned there was plenty of hot water, is that still true?"

"Oh yeah, plenty of hot water."

I noticed the quiet. No ranchera music playing. No soap operas in the background.

"Is it usually this quiet?"

"Oh, yes, very quiet." Relieved, I mentally crossed off two worries from my list.

"Do you mind if I use the bathroom?"

"Sure. Right down the hall."

Inside the bathroom, I noted the roll of toilet paper. I studied the toilet. I flushed. *Voila!* The toilet paper swirled around and disappeared. I was ecstatic at the fine piece of modern plumbing I had discovered.

The house tour continued. We ascended the spiral staircase, passing by a hallway of rooms, all with their doors closed. The only stop we made was to peek into a bedroom whose door was slightly ajar. "This room is where the flight attendants are. They all work for *Aeromexico*. I think there are five, or is it six?" He gazed up at the ceiling deep in thought.

I stuck my head in. "There are only two beds."

"Yeah, their flight schedules and sleep times are all different so it all works out."

We climbed another flight of stairs. "This is where my room is." Alfonso swung open the door to his penthouse, airy and separate. "It may seem like the best room in the house because it is. I collect the rent from all twelve renters and believe me, it's a job." He pointed to the ceiling. "Let's go up to your room."

We climbed a narrower staircase that spiraled to the uppermost room, a room on the roof.

Alfonso pushed the door open. "Take a look around."

Truthfully, there wasn't much to see. A lonesome light bulb hung from the ceiling. A blot of a bed, a dot of a dresser and a whiff of a window facing the street.

"Well?" Alfonso stood in the doorway, his hand on the doorknob.

"Ahm . . . It's . . . uh . . . I was kind of looking for something a bit bigger."

"Oh, but it has a great view of the street. Go look out the window."

I walked two tiny strides to the open window and poked my head out. From the roof, I could see all the people and cars passing by on the street and anyone who pressed the intercom buttons at the front gate. It felt like I was standing on a cloud and peering down at people from a bird's point of view. I gasped. He was right about the view.

I spun around. "When can I sign the lease?"

Alfonso wasted no time loosening the lease that he had squeezed under his armpit. "Here you go."

Apparently, snagging the room to rent was a mere formality with a contact from the inside, which I did, thanks to Malena. I handed over my security deposit. This was to be my new home for a year, Alfonso said, but I had to share it with twelve other housemates.

"Twelve?" I repeated to myself, as though I were a nomad suddenly faced with a 30-year mortgage. That seemed like a very large number for roommates. Suddenly, with the security deposit in Alfonso's hands, my legs began to tremble. "Do these twelve people know each other?"

He frowned. "No, we share the same address, that's all."

"I see. Mind if I read over the fine print of the lease?" I pretended to read over the lease, but what I really wanted was more time to worry. Or rather, to calm my nerves. The Drunk Husband in my first apartment flashed through my mind because I didn't ask enough questions. Now I would be living with twelve people I didn't know. That meant twelve possible things that could go wrong. But, I reminded myself, you'll be living on a lovely street named Ralph Waldo Emerson. What could go wrong with a street named *that*? I pressed my pen in a signature on the dotted line.

I moved in that afternoon.

A month went by before I concluded that I had made an extremely good choice. I could go weeks without seeing other housemates. I was able to say to myself, "Alone at last!" Because their activities were going on under me, I didn't hear a thing. The only time I really noticed that I wasn't living alone was when I went into the kitchen to eat and opened my cupboard and my sweet bread was gone. That food thief again had taken my large round bun. I truly believed this sweet bread was the greatest thing since chocolate chip cookies were invented, and was my new most coveted staple in Mexico. No wonder it gets snatched up. Or if I opened the refrigerator door and my leftovers were gone. The food thief again. I would catch the thief one of these days, I promised myself. Outside of my missing food, I supposed it was as close to peace and harmony as I would get in a city of twenty million.

I was feeling very grateful for being able to sleep soundly in my new bed when one morning an eerie and prolonged whistle sounded from the street. I bolted upright, threw off the covers, and staggered to the window to view the street below.

A knife peddler was wheeling up the street on his bicycle and cart of knives. Before my very eyes and before my tormented ears, the knife sharpener took another humongous breath and blew out his lungs again, that same long and mournful whistle. Clearly, he wanted everybody to know within hearing range of the New York City that he was *a sus órdenes*, at your service. Who on earth needs his knife sharpened at this hour?

The lady across the street apparently did. "*Señor, ahorita me bajo,*" yelled a lady sticking her head out of the window from a house across the street. "I'm coming down right now."

That was it. I couldn't believe it. Sleeping a second more than 4:46 a.m. was definitely, absolutely, and undoubtedly over. I would go to work early even if the office was still covered in shadows. I didn't care. I'd twiddle my thumbs there.

Groggily, I dressed, and was staggering down the stairs when I spotted an Aeromexico flight attendant tiptoeing up the steps. She was clutching her red high heels in one hand and in the other, was biting off a chunk of MY SWEET BUN!

"Aha!" I screeched, pointing a finger at her. "It's *you*! The food thief!"

Her high heels dropped from her hand and went clunking down the steps.

"That's *my sweet bun!* You're eating *my sweet bun!*"

Her eyes got real big and her mouth got real wide as she popped the last chunk of bread into her mouth in one gulp and swallowed. "What bread?" she asked.

"The one you just *ate*," I sneered. "Caught you in the act! That was *my sweet bun!* So this is where all my food is disappearing to, huh?" My shadowy green eyes met her mascara-smeared ones in total eye-to-eye combat.

"So what? What are you going to do about it?" she snarled.

When I went to speak again, I was surprised to find my voice had turned into a nine-year-old's, the very same voice I used when I caught a girl stealing my chips from my cafeteria tray. "I'm telling Alfonso. I *saw* you. I *caught* you in *the act* of

205

stealing."

"Go right ahead," she said, and continued climbing the stairs until she disappeared into her bedroom, slamming the door. Then she yelled behind the closed door, "How do you know that was your bread anyway?"

"I recognize my sweet bun when I see it!" I screamed back. I *did*. It had a crusty brown sugar topping with grooves that looked like a clamshell. Nobody else in the house kept those sweet buns in the kitchen.

"I want my sweet bread back! You'll pay for it!" I yelled behind her door and left the house for work feeling deprived of my bun. Walking toward the Metro station, I plotted on how to inflict some hideous act of revenge. I would snatch her Aeromexico flight pin. Or her little red cap. Or her cutesy cardigan sweater. Oh, I know, her red high heels. I squeezed my brain real hard to picture the food thief. A blurry image of her appeared. Uh-oh, it dawned on me that I only remembered the vaguest details of what the flight attendant actually looked like. How would I be able to describe her later to Alfonso? She had black hair and chocolate eyes and what else? I wished that a police sketch artist was outside waiting to sketch a detailed picture of her so I could hang a WANTED poster on the refrigerator. What I remembered was that she dropped her red high heels when I caught her in the act and that she had stolen my sweet bread.

I walked briskly, turning down Horacio Street and headed to *Consuela's Bakery*, my favorite bakery in the neighborhood. I hoped it was open. It was barely 6:30 a.m. All this thinking had suddenly made me hungry and my stomach growled really loud for my sweet bread. Not just any bread but that exact sweet bun stolen from right under my nose.

When I had reached *Consuela's* bakery, I yanked open the modest door and the aroma of fresh bread rushed toward me; ovenly, heavenly and calorific.

"*Buenos días*," said the lady behind the counter.

"*Buenos días, Señora. ¿Cómo está?*" I returned. Then I got right down to business. I grabbed the giant silvery tongs and yanked an aluminum tray from a stack. At the sight of the overflowing bins of sweet breads, I began salivating. I lifted one of those tempting sweet breads called *conchas* onto my tray. Since I was at it, I might as well check out the empanadas too. I didn't see any in bins so I asked the bakery lady behind the counter if she even had any.

"We have them over here," she pointed to a corner display case where you had to ask her to retrieve one. "Chicken or pineapple?"

"Pineapple? I had never heard of a pineapple empanada. When Marcelo and I . . . I stopped myself. A flash of Marcelo and I laughing with empanadas in our mouths, half-eaten on our plates, empanadas dancing around our heads like half-moons, as I remembered the beautiful Sunday afternoons we spent eating empanadas at our favorite bakery.

"Señorita, which empanadas do you want?" the bakery lady was asking me with her tongs ready to snatch an empanada out the case.

"I'm sorry," I told her. "I'll pass on the empanadas today. *Discúlpame.* Thanks, anyway." I paid a few pesos for my sweet bread and rushed out.

Continuing my journey to work and nibbling on my sweet bread. I was thinking, who gives a *whit* about empanadas, anyway?

I descended and came out of the Metro station on Bucareli Street, and it was only seven o'clock. I was already tired. And there was more action on this street than all the commotion on Emerson put together. I thought my neighborhood was the only place in full swing with the knife sharpener puncturing my eardrums at such an early hour.

No, Buchareli Street was hopping, too. By the looks of it, I had stumbled upon the headquarters of the newspaper deliverymen. Muscular workers whooshed by, pushing wooden dollies and hustling to load and unload bundles of newspapers. *Uno, dos, tres,* a man in a blue apron was hunched over a bundle in deep concentration. He appeared to be the official counter of the newspaper stacks as I studied him

207

thumb through newspaper piles and pencil in the final count on a clipboard in his hand. A row of men were sorters and were putting the various sections of the paper together, the sports section behind the "Mexico in debt section" behind the "Mexico and democracy" section. Young boys, loaded down with bundles of newspapers, hopped on their bikes and whizzed away to their assigned newsstands.

So this is what happened to news after reporters like me went to bed? The printing press took over followed by newspaper delivery men and after that, our dear readers. This city never sleeps either. New York couldn't claim exclusive rights to that idea.

I arrived at the office and turned on my computer. At work at such an early hour, I felt a kindred spirit with all these morning people; the knife sharpener, the bakery lady and newspaper workers. Maybe waking up early wasn't so bad after all. I especially loved my room on the roof. A profoundly peaceful feeling settled on me, even if the flying food thief made me raving mad. I was feeling a part of the hustle of New York, but in an entirely new city.

22

Just Friends

I would not be seduced. I didn't know if it was obvious to others but it was obvious to me. Ashok wanted to be romantic again even though he was saying he just wanted to be friends. Why else would he rent a boat to float down the polluted Xochimilco canals with me? This was a touristy trappy thing to do and Ashok wasn't one to spend a peso more than he had to. There had to be a secret motive at play and I intended to uncover it. While he was telling me about the "big surprise" of going to the floating gardens, I point blank asked him. "What about your Indian girl, the one from the Boston Brahmin family that you're going to marry?"

He stopped his enthusiastic appeal to study my face intently. "What? What are you talking about?"

"Remember? You told me about her. Your-to-be Brahmin wife. *Her.*"

"Oh, she's in the future-future."

"Well, what about the present?" I snapped.

"Speaking of which. What happened to your Mexican Cupid?"

"Who?"

"You know who. The one with the long hair and the fake British accent."

"Are you referring to a gentleman by the name of José?"

"Yeah, José."

"His British accent wasn't fake. I'll have you know, he lived in London where he learned his English. He can recite whole chunks of Shakespeare. Even the sonnets."

"Okay, what happened to Shakespeare?"

"Everything that came out of his mouth was full of sexual innuendos. Just like the real Shakespeare."

"Oh?"

"Yeah. And for your information, our relationship is in the past. Past-past."

"Hmm." His face suddenly brightened. "Well? Does that mean a yes to going with me to Xochimilco then?"

I sighed one long deep sigh. "I guess so. But, as in *just friends*."

That's how I ended up in Xochimilco with Ashok. Going out *one time only* and nothing else. No romance to it.

We were sitting on wooden benches in a flat-bottomed boat while the oarsman paddled down the canal. Our canoe-like boat, a *trajinera*, was painted a gaudy neon yellow and red and named Lolita. It was moving real slow when Ashok began to hum.

While he was humming away, I was still brooding. So you think you can play around with me, Mr. Guru from India, do you? You're mistaken, you'll see. I shook my head at a señora floating by selling flowers on her canoe. Shook my head at the candied-apple boat floating by. Shook my head at the overpriced mariachis drifting by.

"Why not?" Ashok asked me as the musicians floated past. He turned around and motioned the mariachis over to our boat, "*Vénganse*. Come here."

How dare he? Who does he think wants a serenade? Not me. "Why did you call the Mariachis over? This isn't a romantic adventure or anything."

"Why are trying to be so obstinate?" he asked.

Once the musicians got near our canoe, one asked, "Do you have a request?"

"How about *Bésame Mucho?*" Ashok ventured.

They struck up the tune of "*Bésame Mucho.*"

I sat watching the paunchy men stuffed in tight suits, like casings of sausage. They sang their hearts out. *Kiss Me A Lot.* One punctuated the melody with emotional exclamation points and with an occasional prolonged howl "AaaiiiiiiYAJAJAJAAAAAIIIIIIIIIIIIIIIIIIII!!

Ashok paid them a tip, and the Mariachis floated toward someone else's boat. We were outside of earshot when Ashok turned to me. "Explain why you are so grumpy."

"I don't feel like explaining," I told him.

"I'm waiting." Ashok looked at me expectedly.

"Explaining takes too much energy," I mumbled, and then drew a long breath. "You know . . . before coming to Mexico . . ." I stopped. I just couldn't. I didn't want to.

"Go on." He grabbed a bottle of Bohemia from the beer bucket placed in our boat at the beginning of our ride, plucked the cap off, and handed it to me. "Here. You need one."

"Thanks," I said, reaching for the beer bottle, "but I don't *need* it, okay? I want it. That's different." I took a swig and suddenly realized that I felt a bit silly being with Ashok on a boat in Xochimilco. After all, what was going on? It was really bugging me. I needed to know. He was my ex-boyfriend, now colleague, sometimes friend and future who knows what?

"Don't worry. One beer won't ruin your reputation as a teetotaler," Ashok said, mopping his brow.

"You should talk. You are practically an ascetic. You don't eat meat." We sat there, silently sipping our drinks, and looking into each other's eyes. I was fixating on his chin since he was stroking his two whiskers. I was thinking he should really shave those whiskers off. Should I tell him? Nah. Maybe he was growing the beard so we would stay "just friends" and we'd keep at a distance. Still, he was penetrating me with those sepia eyes as if he were taking an X-ray of my insides.

"Let's go up to the Latin American tower afterwards,"

Ashok suddenly said. "I hear it's romantic at night."

"Who wants romantic?"

He sighed, but his eyes were sending out clear radiation waves.

I let his gaze fall all over me like sunlight.

After floating down the canals, we went back to his apartment where Ashok cooked a cauliflower-and-potato curry dinner.

"Ready to go?" Ashok asked after I finished washing the dishes.

"Are you sure you want to pay for another expensive tourist trap?" I asked Ashok.

"Positive." He grinned.

What was wrong with him? So we caught the Metro to the Latin American Tower and when we arrived, found ourselves with a group of Chinese tourists there, snapping pictures on their phones.

"Ashok, we're here with all these tourists."

"Don't pay any attention to the tourists. We're here for the view."

We rode up the forty-four floors to the tower's observation deck with the group of Chinese. They went to one side of the observation deck, and we went to the other side for privacy.

"Wow, it's so beautiful," I said in awe of the panoramic view. The whole city twinkled, like glitter in a sky of black. "You know how this city looks?"

"How?"

"Much better at night."

"I agree. Millions of human beings down there, scattered, scuttling about like ants." Ashok said.

"It makes me feel so puny in the big scheme of things." While meditating on the meaning of life, Ashok stood behind me and ran his fingers slowly back and forth along the length of my neck.

A tingle ran up the back of my neck.

He continued stroking my neck lovingly and in a soft voice said, "You are a great mystery. Mysterious like the universe.

Like the night sky in this megapolis. And I love to read a great mystery."

I turned around. "What is that supposed to mean?" My eyes rested on his twinkling eyes. My pulse was pumping.

"I wish we had met earlier in our lives." His fingers migrated to my waist. He pulled me hard to press his body against mine.

I was breathing heavily into his face when I whispered. "You made it clear. You have plotted your future. I don't want to be your mystery novel."

A few Chinese tourists had gathered around us and were giving us a tsk-tsk-task look for our public displays of affection.

"They're looking at us, Ashok."

"Let them look."

I turned to stare the dozen eyes down. One tourist looked away and started talking to his wife.

"They're talking about us."

"Let them talk," Ashok said. "They're speaking Chinese and we have no clue what they're saying. So who cares?"

"What were you saying, Ashok, before we got stared at?"

"If only . . ." he fumbled for words as he clasped his hands over my cheeks and drew me near for a warm kiss.

The kiss turned my innards to mush. My brain went into a total power outage. "I were Indian," I said, finishing his sentence in a barely audible breath after the kiss. "Say it. That's what you're thinking. If only I were Indian."

"That's not what I was saying."

"If only . . . I had more choice."

I pulled away. "What are you talking about, Ashok?"

"I'm planning to move to Boston in March."

"What? Boston? You're planning to leave Mexico in just three months? So now you're telling me? *I get it.* Why not have one last fling with the *tontita*, the little American idiot, before you go to Boston and marry your Brahmin wife? Is that it, Ashok?"

"No, that's not it."

"It *is* it."

He shook his head.

"*That's it*, isn't it?"

"No, I told you, it's . . . more complicated than that."

"Is it something like it then?" my voice softened a little.

"No, it's *quite* complicated. Sara, I'm attracted to you, so attracted to you that you won't believe it. Do you get that?"

"Yeah, that makes it even worse. So?"

"There's this parental guilt in my head."

"Oh? I know all about parental guilt. My parents lay a guilt trip on me all the time."

"No, I mean, Indian parents know how to *truly* guilt-trip their kids. They *live* to guilt-trip their kids. Trust me, I've seen American parents. They are amateurs."

"You think so? Ha!"

"Yeah, you have to trust me on that one. Because . . . It's . . ." He paused and searched for words. "It's what prevents me from loving you."

Loving me? My bottom lip went into a deep tremble. "Well . . ." I didn't know what to say after that. Love had existed as a foreign word for nearly two years. But he said he *couldn't love me* so it technically means *he doesn't love* me. Which means that love is still a foreign word. So now what are you going to do, Sara?

Suddenly, I felt little again, about the age when a grown up starts nagging you with the ultimate existential question, *what do you want to be when you grow up?* As a kid, I could never answer that, and I still couldn't answer it. I finally found some words. "I might go back to New York too. I've been thinking about it recently."

"What would you do if you go back?" Ashok asked.

See. There it is. That existential question. "I'm not sure."

"You should write human features or do investigative stuff. You're good at that."

Tears welled up in my eyes. I didn't want to cry. I felt something for Ashok and didn't want the creature inside of me to escape. "I got dumped before I moved to Mexico," I blurted out of nowhere, like I had just unloaded seventy-five pounds.

His liquidy dark eyes were all compassion. "Getting dumped is terrible," Ashok said in a soft voice, "and universal.

Actually, it's more like universally terrible."

"Well, it *was* terrible."

"I'm sorry, Sara." Ashok said.

"It's over. Nothing but an old flame." I didn't want one molecule of sympathy. I was done with that.

"Oh." Ashok looked at me, and appeared not to believe it. "So you're over him."

"I think so. It wasn't a healthy relationship to begin with. My pity parties have gone away."

"Always a good sign." Ashok said. "That's why it was so hard for you to tell me about him back when we were in the boat today? I sensed you had been hurt ever since the first time we went out."

"Well, so now it's confirmed. Maybe the hurt never totally goes away. And let me tell you, it kind of feels like I'm being dumped by you right now. Not in the same way, of course. We haven't really developed a clear relationship between us. Now you're telling me that you want a relationship but you really can't."

"I'm so sorry Sara, I truly am," he whispered, trying to comfort me by burying my head in his chest.

I didn't want my head buried in his chest. My head bobbed up and I looked him straight in the eye. "No, I like brutal honesty over lies. I handle it better."

"You do?"

"Yes. We can be just friends, can't we?"

"Right. Isn't that what you said you wanted anyway?" Ashok asked.

"Yeah, but in my opinion, you were really mixing up the signals."

"Sorry."

"Just friends from now on."

Ashok nodded. "Without the *just* though," he said. "A friend is precious."

After Ashok dropped me off at my apartment that night, I couldn't sleep. I reflected on how I had come a long way since New York and having my heart broken by Marcelo. My heart hadn't completely healed, but I had seriously downgraded Marcelo. Enough to tell Ashok that Marcelo was "an old flame" and not "the love of my life." That meant I was in much better shape than before. And I had another friend besides Malena. Ashok.

I was tempted to get out of bed and update my resume.

23

Jane Bond on a Mission

I t all started with a call from a tabloid wanting to know who Bonecrusher's girlfriend was. How on earth was I supposed to know? Who was Bonecrusher, anyway? I soon discovered he was a famous American boxer who was spending the weekend with a beautiful woman who was not his wife in Mexico City.

Well, you could throw me as far away as you can get from sports, let alone ask me to cover an American boxer named Bonecrusher.

"Are you sure you've called the right reporter?" I asked the editor of the tabloid. "I don't usually cover sports." The editors must have called every reporter in town and had been turned down. No respectable journalist would be caught dead working for a tabloid. If you are a respectable journalist, you think publications like *The National Dirt* make things up, and whatever dirt they uncover is not real news but media scum.

"Well, are you going to take it?" The editors were serious, however, and they were begging. In their cry for help, they chose me the hack, the desperate-for-money kind of reporter, to be the snoop to get the information on the girl. In other words, I would be their *spy*. Spying on a heavyweight world champion sounded thrilling and terrifying at the same time. "Which girl are we talking about?"

"*The other woman*," the editor of the tabloid explained as if I had some kinks in the brain to work out. "We want you to get her first and last name."

"Oh? *The other woman?*" The other woman business had a distantly familiar ring to it. Something that I had wanted to erase, like shaking an Etch-a-Sketch real hard and the past was gone, but with a phone call, it had suddenly come back to life. "Um, can I think about this and get back to you?"

"We need to know if you can do it now," the editor of *The National Dirt* snapped.

I'll admit I was excited to serve on a reconnaissance mission for this tabloid, one of the most widely read rags displayed at Kroger checkout stands all over the U.S., but I sniffed some hidden dangers as well.

"Do you want to hear the details?" the editor of *The National Dirt* was asking. "First, we need to know if you will accept the assignment."

"Now? Er . . . um . . ." I cleared my throat. I could do this. The job wasn't part of a paparazzi chase. No prowling around some hotel room sifting through a trash can for condom wrappers. "What's the pay?" I had to determine if it was worth the high stress.

"One thousand to 1,400 dollars, depending on how much information you can get."

Did my ears have balls of wax in them? I didn't hear that right. I was used to getting paid $150 a week. High reward signaled high risk. What if Bonecrusher caught me, the small-fry reporter, spying on him? It would give him a very good reason to defend his world's heavyweight champion title. "What kind of deadline are we talking about?"

"Tonight, by 10 p.m. You need to be at his hotel in an hour. Oh, you get a free dinner, too."

"An hour?" I clenched the phone tighter, and with my other hand, steadied my knee bumping against the table. "All right,

I'll do it." Then I said "goodbye" as quick as I could.

Oh, my God! What am I going to do with the money I'm going to get?? I'm going to buy the building. No, wait! I'm going to buy the block. No. wait. I'm going to buy a penthouse in Manhattan!

I looked at my watch. "Oh, my God!"

I raced around my bedroom snapping clothes off hangers and flinging them on the bed. Should I dress in camouflage? In olive and beige to blend into the walls? I checked my watch. I had exactly 58 minutes to make it to the hotel. There was no time to waste. My future fortune was at stake. I threw on a blue dress.

Minutes later, I dashed down the stairs, up the street, and down the Metro steps. I dashed out of the train, up the steps and down the street. I dashed into the hotel and directly into the hotel receptionist.

"Whoa!" the receptionist said. "Take it easy."

Clawing at her hotel counter, I was panting, "I made it! Please tell me I made it."

"Let me guess," she said, and motioned to a group of people milling outside the elevator. "You're here for a glimpse of Bonecrusher like the rest of the crowd?"

"How did you know?" I wheezed, scratching my legs that were on fire.

"He should be coming down any minute."

Sure enough, Bonecrusher and his entourage strutted out of the elevator into the hotel lobby at that moment.

Without a boxer's robe, trunks or boxing gloves, Bonecrusher was fully dressed in jeans and shirt, but with knees bent and a testosterone surplus in his biceps, and clearly strutting. His right ear was shaped like a broccoli floret, fibrous, tough and deformed. Just by one scary look at him, I was certain he could pick me up with one hand and sail me across the room, and then later, scatter my bone parts around the hotel lobby in a deeply scientific way.

"There he is," the receptionist said in a half whisper.

Staring at his biceps made swallowing difficult. It made me

want to locate the nearest window, climb out onto a fire escape and slide quietly down the sidewalk and run as fast as I could toward home. Instead, I moved with the wave of fan crush and entourage and tried to blend in while carefully eyeing Bonecrusher. My job was not to let the Macho Man out of my sight for a second.

Bonecrusher strutted by with two model-like Barbie girls. One on each arm, like bench presses. Oh, my God, nobody told me there would be two women. Which one was his girlfriend or *the other woman?*

He strutted, paused, and kissed one Barbie on the lips. Then strutted a few more steps, paused, and kissed the other Barbie on the lips.

His agent announced to all of us in the lobby that a small group of invited fans would be following Bonecrusher to dinner, which would be in the hotel's restaurant.

I trailed the entourage, frightened to death. *He's going to find me out, I just know it. I can feel it in my bones.* What if he starts asking me questions, what if he asks me how I got here, what if he asks me something about boxing?

If he found me out, I pictured Bonecrusher sitting on my shoulders, wrapping his legs around my throat, and with hyperextended arms, I would fall backward to the floor—essentially—dead. Which means I'd end up bone broth.

I sat in a chair at the end of a long table to blend it with his entourage who apparently thought I was an invited guest. The waiter came around. My brain was blinking yellow, warning me to focus on the difference between wrestling and boxing so I just said, "I'll have whatever everyone else is having."

T-bone steaks came. I took a stab at my bleeding-piece-of-meat, politely put my fork down, and studied each girl as if I had drone antennas and they were sending me secret radio signals. Which one was the woman not to worry about, and which was *the one* to worry about, *the other woman?*

Suddenly, mariachis burst into the dining room. They asked the boxer to please give them the honor of playing just one song for him. Throughout the whole mariachi song, one girl never took her adoring eyes off Bonecrusher. *Aha!* That had to be her. That was *the other woman!*

After the mariachis went back to the bar area, I strained to block out the background chatter and listen to *the other woman* talk. Based on bits of conversation and hearing her accent, I guessed she was from Michigan, my home state, or at least somewhere in the Midwest. As soon as she gets up to go the bathroom, I'll follow her, I told myself. I'll corner her at the sink. Ask her some questions.

Had two bites of my Caveman meal before a window of opportunity arrived. The woman was excusing herself to go to the ladies' room so I nonchalantly shoved my chair back and tagged after her. I flushed the toilet in the stall and hurried out. And then, I cornered her at the sink. I let her wash her hands first, of course, before I zeroed in on her blue eyes with the longest lashes I had ever seen. Mascara overload. So I pulled out my mascara to refresh and said in the most irritated voice I could muster, "Man, mascara is such a pain. It always flakes off and bothers my eyes."

"Oh, mine too," she said.

"I'm Sara, and you are?"

"Lisa," she said in a guarded tone.

"You sound like you're from Detroit."

"Close. Chicago."

"Nice to meet you." Then, suddenly, she must have sensed that she had slipped because fear flashed in her eyes. She turned and hurried out of the bathroom.

The evening was over and I failed to extract her last name. I rushed home and phoned *The National Dirt.* "Lisa something, from Chicago," I told them. The tabloid had already found out the last name from another reporter who had been at the dinner, too. Geez, who could that have been? I began to worry that the tabloid would make me split the big money with someone else.

Two weeks later, this sensational bit of news was splashed on the tabloid's front page in the magazine rack right next to the candy shelf and the gums. Alex picked up a copy of *The*

National Dirt at the supermarket to see Bonecrusher in the newspaper. Next to the headings TOM'S HOUSE OF HORRORS and ANGELINA ADOPTS ALIEN BABY was a three-inch BONECRUSHER CHEATS ON WIFE IN MEXICO with a photo of the heavyweight champion and a Barbie girl on each arm. Each of their names was printed in boldface in the photo caption.

Soon after that, I received a check for $1,000. It was my Jane Bond Moment.

24

Lucky Red Underwear

New Year's Eve rolled around again. Time to do inventory. Things I might want to forget but wouldn't: my operation, the earthquake tremor, the unpleasant break-up with José. Things I wanted to remember: my friendship with Malena and Ashok, the Mayan ruins, a city unvarnished at dawn.

With nowhere to go by late afternoon, I was about to turn on some wacky Mexican television when, at the last minute, Malena called and saved me from the sufferfest. She invited me to her house but warned me she had no cardboard horns to squeak, no confetti to toss in the air and no cone-shaped party hats to wear. "We'll have a pot of tamales. Would that be okay?"

"Sure, I'll bring something to eat, too. Don't worry. I don't miss that party stuff." Well, that was mostly true. I wasn't homesick for the bands and pop stars that I usually watched on television in New York. But I missed a person next to me to kiss at midnight and sing "Auld Lang Syne." Still, I had an invitation to get out of the house and I was going.

When Malena brought out her mother's steaming pot of

homemade tamales, I surprised her by uncovering my bowl of homemade salsa. Malena stuck her finger in the bowl and I looked at her and waited. "So, what do you think?"

"Hmm, I'm still tasting . . ."

"So, what do you think?"

"Did you put the exact number of jalapeños I wrote down?" I nodded. "So what do you think?"

"I think," she said, licking her finger, "it's damn good."

I grinned. "You mean it?"

"Yes! I mean it!"

"She said yes, she did, I heard a yes!" I wiggled my hips, and pumped my fists in the air. "Move over, Tabasco sauce, Maria's salsita, Conchita's zingy."

"Wow. Talk about overreacting," Malena said.

Never mind. My victory dance continued. "My lip-tingling salsa has taken over. It's center stage."

"I didn't say *that.*"

After I settled down, we finished our tamales dripping with *my salsa.* My intention was not to put a damper on the evening, but I told Malena that even though I wanted to stay in Mexico, I was nearing a fundless and therefore, funless state. I had paid off my medical expenses with my paycheck from the tabloid, but it had me thinking about returning to New York. I seemed to remain permanently broke. Foreign correspondents working for the U.S. dailies in Mexico got paid like I had for *The National Dirt,* but I wasn't sure a foreign correspondent's job would ever come my way. The Associated Press offered me a full-time job in New York and I was going to take it.

"Do you want to hear how I calculated my money situation and my professional success here?" I pulled out a grimy piece of paper from my pocket.

"Sure," she agreed but with less than wholehearted enthusiasm.

"To save money, I've eaten at least 1,400 tortillas, two a day in two years' time, but probably many, many more.

"Yeah," Malena said, listening carefully. "So?"

"In the span of two years, I would estimate that in sheer

square footage alone, I've eaten enough tortillas to stretch from here to Anchorage, Alaska. Now comparing my fame and acclaim in square footage, that would only go from here to Baja, California. You see? It all adds up."

"So what are you saying, chica?"

"I'm saying it's clear I'm not going anywhere." I had eaten so many tacos I was a taco shy of winning the Two Thousand Kilometer Taco Tasting Marathon.

"That's why you want to leave Mexico? You're tired of eating tortillas and you're not a famous reporter?"

"Something like that, but mostly I'm tired of being poor." Maybe, because Malena lived on another planet of inherited wealth, she had a hard time relating to my financial situation.

"Okay, maybe you're not *big famous* on the level of Elena Poniatowska."

"Or Oriana Fallaci," I added, "we must include the Italian journalist that interviewed all those famous people."

"Right. But at least in rookie reporter circles, you are kind of *small famous*."

"I am?"

She nodded.

"Well, I can't refuse a reporter's job in New York with double the pay. But I'm also worried about Alex. He needs to get back into chemotherapy. So I've collected photos of hot bald actors. I got Bruce Willis, Samuel Jackson, Stanley Tucci to show him."

"Show him what?"

"Bare heads can be hot."

"Tell him that we have the handsome, hairless dog here in Mexico," Malena added. "Xolo. No, maybe not. Don't tell him that. He might not like be compared to a dog."

"Exactly."

She nodded. "You got a good heart, *chica*. But what you also need is a good pair of red underwear."

"Huh?" I was relieved that I hadn't destroyed all the good will of the evening by talking about my finances, but red underwear made no sense.

"Red underwear, it brings you luck in love. Yellow underwear brings you luck in money."

"Can I have both?" I asked. "I mean, is that what you had in mind for a New Year's surprise?" Maybe the right color of underwear was *the secret* that Victoria was hiding at her lingerie store.

"No, silly, I didn't buy you any underwear. Sorry."

"That's okay. It was weird, anyway."

"But I have a different surprise for you later on."

"Really? You know how I love surprises."

A few minutes before midnight, Malena pulled out a big bowl of purple grapes. She divided the grapes into two smaller bowls with twelve grapes in each one. She slid one bowl across the table. "They'll bring good luck to you, if you pop them in your mouth one by one."

"You mean one grape per second?" My New Year's Eve began to take on all the excitement of a space shuttle at liftoff. It beat watching a glittery Times Square ball by a long shot.

"Yes, a countdown. Gulping grapes, got it?"

"Got it. Preparing for launch, see?" I showed Malena my grape pinched between my fingers. Even if I wasn't getting any lucky yellow or red underwear, I wasn't about to pass up a humble ritual to ensure me twelve happy months ahead. This would be a cinch to do. One grape for each month of good luck for the New Year. We both eyed the clock.

"*Lista?*"

"Ready."

At exactly twelve seconds before midnight, Malena shouted, "Twelve!" She popped a single grape in her mouth.

I popped a grape into my mouth.

"Eleven!" she shouted.

Another grape disappeared into our mouths. Popped in one, popped in two, popped in three—pitching grapes into my mouth as fast as I could like baseballs in a batting cage.

"Make a wish for each grape you swallow," Malena instructed.

"I am." I coughed.

"Are you making a wish?" and she stretched her neck in eager expectation of the next grape.

I nodded and gulped.

"Nine!" she shouted.

"We're already on nine? I asked, chewing as fast as I could. In the demanding exercise of grape gulping and chewing, I discovered that one second was not quite long enough to pop a grape in my mouth, chew it a bit, and then swallow it. The grapes had seeds in them. I was almost swallowing them and practically choking.

"What do I do with the seeds?" I spluttered.

"Chew or spit 'em out!" Malena mumbled, still chewing.

Though I failed to finish eating my twelve grapes in the countdown to midnight, I couldn't stop laughing. I wasn't chewing them fast enough and what was worse, I tried talking to Malena while chewing.

"*¡Feliz año nuevo!*" Happy New Year! We gave each other a kiss on both cheeks and a big hug.

Fireworks crackled in the sky outside. I sighed. I was looking forward to a very happy new year. And although I didn't really believe in those superstitions, I figured that the next time I replaced my underwear, I might as well go for some in red and some in yellow. My luck might change.

* * *

A week later, I made a decision. It was time to either sell a kidney or go home. I really wanted my kidney, and I would miss Mexico but I needed to earn more money in the States. I booked my flight to New York.

And before you know it, I was arranging and rearranging my colorful Mexican dresses and skirts—in bright reds and blues and yellows—in my suitcase. In went my news clippings, which I guarded with my life, since I hadn't lined up a job yet in New York. In went a papier-mâché figurine of an old man for Alex and in went colorful clay pottery for my family. With both anticipation and sadness, I flung myself on the bed to gaze at my one suitcase and reflect on my Mexican experience.

I was leaving a part of me in Mexico: fibroids, friends, and most of all, the feelings that I arrived with. I also hoped to leave some goodwill toward Americans. Mexico was less mysterious to me, but it was full of complexity that I had not even scratched. I was semi-chile literate. At least I could tell three chiles apart: chiles poblanos from jalepeños from chiles de árbol. And from Malena's judgment, I made a decent salsa; medium hot with jalapeño, onion, garlic, lemon juice and olive oil and cut up tomatoes in squares. After all, my time in Mexico was not only about figuring out a new culture, but also figuring out myself.

One of the gifts I took away from living in Mexico was a greater awareness of all things related to my emotions. I felt more comfortable expressing my feelings in Mexico and I'd especially miss that part about the culture. Whenever excitement or sadness overwhelmed me in New York, I was usually told "Calm down," "Don't get excited," "Lower your voice," or "Don't be so emotional." The head, not the heart, ruled. Unlike here. I would miss the people who had been warm and accepting of me and took me as I was.

Two years earlier, I was a different person. Mexico had given me the start of a new career, Spanish language skills, and with all those hours of line-standing, seat-warming, and thumb-twiddling, I could say without any exaggeration whatsoever, I was going with a lifetime supply of patience. I learned the secrets of the little now, the suspension of time, fully experiencing and enjoying life in the present moment.

I wanted to stop by the cactus garden inside the grounds of the National Palace before leaving for New York. Mexicans consider the cactus or *nopal*, to be a a "Life-Giving Plant" This plant has given Mexicans so much; its red, purple and yellow flowers of beauty, its fruit to savor, its pads to enjoy roasted or cut up in quesadillas and salads, its juice so full of minerals and fiber that's so good for your health and oh, so many other vital things. To me, it has been a symbol of Mexico, for Mexico has given me so much.

I didn't plan to scratch out my initials on the cactus pad. Forget adding initials of a boyfriend intertwined with mine like so many couples do. A new boyfriend had eluded me. No, I'd carve out a big heart on the cactus that meant "I Love You, Mexico." I would draw a whole heart, not a broken one, to thank the people for giving me all the friendships that I've had with them. All my experiences in Mexico have healed me and made me whole again. Perhaps I'd draw the heart with some dents, just like the cactus plant naturally has on its pads, to show that my heart has healed, but, like skin, would remain a bit uneven after a deep cut.

* * *

When I arrived at the Benito Juárez airport days later, I was surrounded by Malena, Ashok, and even Francisco who insisted on coming to the airport to send me off and wish me well. Malena stood by my side stoically waiting for my flight to be called. When the garbled announcement came over the loudspeaker, I threw my arms around her neck. "I'm going to miss you, Malena, I mean it, really miss you."

"Take care of yourself, *chica*, and write. Promise?"

I hugged her harder. I would have crushed every rib in Malena's body if she hadn't shaken off my clutch.

"Enough drama. Remember me, okay?"

"Of course, I will!" Wiping my eyes with my scarf to hide my tears, Malena still turned into a blur. "Thanks for being such a good friend."

"Damn. Do I need a cigarette right now," Malena said and fumbled in her purse for her pack.

Then Ashok and Francisco wet both my cheeks with their kisses and followed up with hearty hugs.

"I will miss all of you. Really. I'll miss Mexico. You have been very, very kind. A thousand thank-you's. *Mil gracias.*"

"*Cuídate mucho,*" Ashok said. Take care of yourself.

Francisco winked. "Don't forget your Spanish"

"I won't."

"I'll never forget you and our mission to find statues of Cortés and Malinche."

"That certainly was an adventure, wasn't it? Hey, Francisco, thanks for everything. I owe all my Spanish to you."

"*No hay de que*," Francisco said. It was nothing.

"*Vaya con Dios*," Malena added. Go with God. The unlit cigarette fell from her fingers.

"I am going with God, blessed and all." My voice cracked as another string of thank you's dropped from my mouth and scattered to my new friends until I boarded the American Airlines flight to New York City.

Once inside the cabin of the plane, I sniffed a little but wiped away all evidence of that tearful goodbye. The contrast of the elaborate displays of affection to the stillness of the cabin was stark. I was a stranger in this cramped and stuffy place. I bumped down the aisle, found 15C and fastened my seat belt. My seat and the tray were so clean they bordered on sterile. Had I accidentally stepped into a hospital operating room? The fluorescent lights shone too bright.

Once we took off, I pulled out the book I was reading and gave a few loving pats to my healed chest, a little off center, to the left, where my heart resides. My broken heart was back in one piece. I considered the sealed cracks nothing but a healthy dose of cynicism about romantic love. And I had recovered the taste of happiness.

The flight attendants served us square, round and triangular portions of foodstuffs that came in space-age packages like astronauts eat. I spit out my chicken entree that I had bit into and asked myself, "What is this? Listerine?" Shivering, I turned the knob of the air conditioning blasting from my overhead vent.

Fifty pages into my book, my attention turned to the deafening silence. Nobody moved. Besides the nervous teenager behind me clearing his throat every 15 seconds, nearly everyone else on the plane looked on the verge of being a senior citizen. Was there no baby or toddler in sight? Could I get some noise, please? I laughed at myself, and how much I had really changed. Before I went to Mexico, I remember how terrified I was seeing parents board with toddlers or babies and carried earplugs just in case I was bombarded with their cries.

Alex picked me up at the airport.

"Am I staying with you tonight?"

"Got to. Don't you remember? You have no apartment to return to."

"Oh, my God, you're right." Of course, I remembered that I had lost my apartment when my landlord had found out about my illegal sublet, but it hadn't sunken in.

"Cynthia gave away all your furniture and remaining possessions."

"She gave away all my books?" My voice rose to hysteria. "Why didn't you tell me?"

"Calm down! You don't remember. I saved them for you."

"Oh." I let out a sigh of relief.

When we arrived at Alex's apartment, I couldn't wait to give him my little gift. I unzipped my suitcase to find the clay pottery broken and in pieces. I had so carefully packed was in shards.

"I packed them so carefully, Alex," I said, unwrapping the newspaper and placing the pieces on the floor.

"Wouldn't you know it, there goes my gift to everyone in Michigan," I said. "They'll never believe me if I tell them I bought them something, but it ended up all broken."

Alex laughed. "I'll be your witness to your shattered shards."

I dug through the bright skirts to unearth the figurine of the old man. "Here, you go." I handed it to my cousin. "He's made of papier-mâché and still intact. I know he's a bit morbid, but I hope you like him."

"He isn't morbid. Just very serious. And very old. A hard worker, I would imagine, carrying that big pot. It's amazing how they can make a face so detailed out of papier-mâché."

I found myself grinning. "Yeah, it's one of the many folk arts in Mexico. You find them everywhere."

"He's so special. I'll have to find a special place to put him,"

Alex said, and when he thought I wasn't looking, he wiped away a tear.

* * *

For days, New York was a strange country, and I was a newly arrived foreigner. I wandered into each room of Alex's apartment and then forgot why I was there. I started to look for little clues. There was a sink, a toilet that could flush with paper in it. I looked around. I hoped I had made the right decision in coming back to the U.S.

At least I arrived in New York skinnier. I hadn't even glanced at a brownie in two whole years. I hadn't microwaved a burrito. I hadn't bitten into a bag of Doritos in a long, long time.

More than anything, I found myself desperately needing to talk about my adventures in Mexico, the good and the bad, with my old friends in New York. When I got together with my co-workers Cynthia and Derek, over tortilla chips, guacamole and my homemade salsa one evening, I was telling them about one of the things I noticed that was different about Mexico. "You see, New Yorkers spend all their time rushing around while Mexicans spend all their time waiting around," I ventured, dipping my tortilla chip in the tingly salsa.

"Yeah . . . so?" Cynthia asked.

"Well, Mexicans have this gesture they use to make you wait." I showed them the forefinger and thumb an inch apart, the "*ahorita*" gesture. It means "a little now."

"That's nice," Cynthia said.

"So you don't think that's funny?"

She shook her head.

"Uh . . . was it supposed to be?" Derek asked, dipping his tortilla chip in the guacamole dip.

"You know the Spanish word for avocado?"

Cynthia volunteered. "Isn't it *aguacate?*"

I nodded.

"I knew that," Derek said, popping the green-smothered

tortilla chip in his mouth. "But it's really a Nahuatl word for testicles."

Derek's eyes grew saucer big. He stopped chewing.

Shocked, Cynthia asked. "You're kidding, aren't you?"

"Nah, I'm not," I said, and turned to Derek. "I'm afraid that you're eating testicle sauce."

He spit out bits of his chip onto his plate. "Why did you have to go and tell me that? You, my friend, are evil. I might never want to eat guacamole again."

"Oh, come on. It's because of the avocado's shape. The Aztecs believed the fruit possessed aphrodisiac qualities."

Derek was left speechless.

"I'll pass on eating anymore testicle sauce," Cynthia said in a low voice.

I had imparted cultural knowledge and shocked my New York friends at the same time. I was happy. I might be misunderstood and without many material goods, but I was rich in experience.

I lay awake thinking about things that night. There was probably nothing to worry about, I told myself. I was just getting used to New York all over again, that's all. I rolled over. It was not long before my heavy eyelids closed and I was dreaming of Mexico.

About the Author

Diane Asitimbay holds a degree in international relations from Michigan State University. As a reporter in Mexico, she wrote for the *Mexico City News* and the international news agency *United Press International.* She has been a guest columnist and writer for numerous magazines and newspapers, and her articles have appeared in *Hispanic, Business Mexico,* and the *San Diego Union-Tribune.* Her books include the non-fiction guide, *What's Up, America?* and a book of poetry, *No Perfect People, Please!* She also teaches English to international students at the University of California – San Diego.

Made in United States
Troutdale, OR
11/23/2024

25224638R00145